Ultimate Millennials' Movie Quiz Book

1500 Questions on Movies from 1990 to 2019

Published by Rashleigh Publishing

ISBN 978-1-8381697-0-1

150 sets of 10 Quiz Questions

There are five different types of quiz in this book:

Standard quiz
Questions are worth from 1 to 10 points - the harder the question the more points you get. Total available for each of these quizzes is 55 points.

Anagrams
Anagrams of films grouped by decade. 1 point for each film identified.

Three Word Descriptions
Films described in three words. 1 point for each film identified.

Cryptic Clues
A cryptic puzzle to work out the film. 1 point for each film identified.

Name 10
Name the 10 items on the list. 1 point for each one identified.

WARNING: THE NATURE OF THE QUESTIONS MEANS THERE WILL BE SOME SPOILERS WITHIN THE QUESTIONS AND ANSWERS!

Categories

1	1990	41	1998
2	Colours	42	News
3	Meryl Streep Movies	43	Sport #1
4	Real Life #1	44	Travel
5	Tom Cruise Movies	45	Weather
6	1991	46	1999
7	Name the Razzie Worst Picture Winner	47	Name the Movie From the Featured Song #1
8	Hugh Grant Movies	48	Nicole Kidman Movies
9	Dawson's Creek Actors	49	Lord of the Rings
10	Magic	50	Drama #1
11	1992	51	2000
12	James McAvoy Movies	52	Adam Sandler Movies
13	Anagrams 1990s	53	These Movies All Have "American" in the Title
14	Jurassic Park Movies	54	Horror #1
15	Leonardo DiCaprio Movies	55	Friends Actors
16	1993	56	2001
17	Cameron Diaz Movies	57	Action #1
18	Name 10 #1	58	Book Adaptations
19	Mark Wahlberg Movies	59	Food
20	Cryptic Clues #1	60	Film Scores / Soundtrack - Name the Composer
21	1994	61	2002
22	Pixar	62	Around the World
23	Harrison Ford Movies	63	James Bond
24	Romcoms	64	Dwayne Johnson Movies
25	Animals #1	65	Numbers
26	1995	66	2003
27	Name the Movie From the Tagline #1	67	Sigourney Weaver Movies
28	Westerns	68	Disney
29	Kate Winslet Movies	69	Anagrams 2000s
30	Space	70	Sylvester Stallone Movies
31	1996	71	2004
32	Thrillers #1	72	Netflix Originals
33	Name the Movie From the Quote #1	73	Remakes
34	Arnie Movies	74	Jim Carrey Movies
35	Where in the World..... #1	75	Christmas Movies
36	1997	76	2005
37	Three Words #1	77	Chris Evans Movies
38	Comedies #1	78	Real Life #2
39	Animation #1	79	Christopher Nolan's Batman Trilogy
40	Bruce Willis Movies	80	Drama #2

Categories

QUESTIONS

1. 1990

1	Macaulay Culkin appeared as Kevin McCallister in which film?	**1 Point**
2	Leonardo, Donatello, Raphael and Michaelangelo made up which foursome?	**2 Points**
3	What song is playing during the famous pottery scene in 'Ghost'?	**3 Points**
4	As what do Robbie Coltrane and Eric Idle dress whilst on the run?	**4 Points**
5	Edward and Vivian are the main characters in which romantic comedy film?	**5 Points**
6	What name does Dunbar give to the wolf he befriends in 'Dances with Wolves'?	**6 Points**
7	To which year do Marty McFly and Doc Brown travel back in 'Back to the Future Part III'?	**7 Points**
8	'Die Hard 2' was set at which airport?	**8 Points**
9	What make of car does Tom Cruise drive in 'Days of Thunder'?	**9 Points**
10	In what town is 'Arachnophobia' set?	**10 Points**

2. Colours

1	What film about basketball starred Woody Harrelson and Wesley Snipes?	**1 Point**
2	In what 1999 film does Martin Lawrence star as a thief trying to retrieve a diamond from a police station?	**2 Points**
3	What 2012 action film starring Chris Hemsworth was a remake of a 1984 film of the same name?	**3 Points**
4	Name the 2006 New Zealand horror film set on a farm.	**4 Points**
5	Mako sharks are made super-intelligent in which film?	**5 Points**
6	Isabela Merced played the title role of which family film from 2019?	**6 Points**
7	The galaxy is on Orion's Belt in which film?	**7 Points**
8	Which 1990 film was based on the 1984 debut novel from one of the world's most famous authors?	**8 Points**
9	Barbara Hershey played the mother of the main character in which 2010 film?	**9 Points**
10	In what film does a retired FBI agent try and track down the serial killer known as 'The Tooth Fairy'?	**10 Points**

3. Meryl Streep Movies

1	Complete the name of the 1995 drama 'The Bridges of...'	**1 Point**
2	Who played the older Dennis Thatcher in 'The Iron Lady'?	**2 Points**
3	What Netflix film from 2019 was about the Panama Papers scandal?	**3 Points**
4	She starred as The Witch in 'Into The Woods', a film based on what fairy tale?	**4 Points**
5	In 'It's Complicated', with whom does she have an affair?	**5 Points**
6	Which real-life person did she portray in 'Suffragette'?	**6 Points**
7	In 'Marvin's Room', what does her sister ask her for when she gets sick?	**7 Points**
8	What was the name of her character in the film 'Doubt', set in a Catholic school?	**8 Points**
9	In 'Florence Foster Jenkins', what was the name of her long-term companion, played by Hugh Grant?	**9 Points**
10	In 'The River Wild', what is the name of the section of the river through which Streep is forced to take the group?	**10 Points**

4. Real Life #1

1	What 2005 film starred Joaquin Phoenix as Johnny Cash?	1 Point
2	Michael Fassbender starred as which tech entrepeneur in a 2015 film?	2 Points
3	'The Founder' starred Michael Keaton as the mastermind behind which restaurant chain?	3 Points
4	Charlize Theron won an Oscar for her portrayal of which serial killer in 'Monster'?	4 Points
5	In 'Lion', an Australian couple adopted Saroo Brierley from which country?	5 Points
6	Which two actors starred as James Hunt and Niki Lauda in 2013's 'Rush'?	6 Points
7	Name the film, based on the memoir of neurologist Oliver Sack, starring Robin Williams as a doctor working with catatonic patients.	7 Points
8	Of which baseball team is Billy Beane the General Manager in 'Moneyball'?	8 Points
9	'Cinderella Man' was about which boxer?	9 Points
10	'My Week with Marilyn' was set during the production of which film?	10 Points

5. Tom Cruise Movies

1	What film is named after and based on a real-life operation to assassinate Hitler in 1944?	**1 Point**
2	Who starred in 'Edge of Tomorrow' as Rita Vrataski, who helped Cruise's character when he was reliving the same day over and over?	**2 Points**
3	Name the film in which he and Andrea Riseborough were two of the last people left on Earth.	**3 Points**
4	At the end of 'Magnolia', what starts falling from the sky?	**4 Points**
5	What is his occupation in 'Lions for Lambs'?	**5 Points**
6	What is the name of the pre-cog which John takes from the facility in 'Minority Report'?	**6 Points**
7	At what sort of store does he track down Sandy in 'Jack Reacher'?	**7 Points**
8	In 'Rock of Ages', what was his band called?	**8 Points**
9	In 'Vanilla Sky', the sky David had chosen for his lucid dream was taken from a painting by which artist?	**9 Points**
10	What is the name of his character in 'Interview with the Vampire'?	**10 Points**

6. 1991

1	Morticia, Gomez, Uncle Fester, Wednesday and Pugsley were more commonly known as who?	**1 Point**

2	Which film was based on a 1963 assassination?	**2 Points**

3	Who starred as the eponymous captain in 'Hook'?	**3 Points**

4	What horror remake culminates on a houseboat?	**4 Points**

5	Who played the detective trying to track down 'Thelma and Louise'?	**5 Points**

6	In what film are Christina Applegate and her siblings left alone all summer?	**6 Points**

7	Which comedy film starred Rik Mayall as an imaginary friend?	**7 Points**

8	Who played 'King Ralph', an American slob who becomes the King of the UK?	**8 Points**

9	In what romcom does a doctor played by Michael J Fox get stuck in a small town?	**9 Points**

10	The music of which composer gives Julia Roberts the chills in 'Sleeping with the Enemy'?	**10 Points**

7. Name the Razzie Worst Picture Winner

1	Erotic 1996 film starring Demi Moore as a stripper.	**1 Point**
2	Halle Berry starred as the title character in this superhero film.	**2 Points**
3	Remake featuring The Thing, The Invisible Woman and The Human Torch.	**3 Points**
4	Final part of the vampire film series based on books by Stephenie Meyer.	**4 Points**
5	Romance film starring Madonna and directed by Guy Ritchie.	**5 Points**
6	Not only did this animated film from 2017 win Worst Picture, it also won Worst Director, Worst Screen Combo and Worst Screenplay.	**6 Points**
7	John Travolta starred in this sci-fi action film, about a rebellion against aliens on Earth.	**7 Points**
8	Ben Affleck and Jennifer Lopez starred together.	**8 Points**
9	1991 action comedy starring Bruce Willis as a cat burglar.	**9 Points**
10	Romantic "comedy" from 2008 starring Mike Myers.	**10 Points**

8. Hugh Grant Movies

1	What colour eyes did Mickey have in the title of the 1999 film?	1 Point
2	What film from 2006 was about a TV music talent competition?	2 Points
3	He starred as the Pirate Captain in 'The Pirates! In an Adventure with Scientists!' produced by which animation studio?	3 Points
4	He played a private investigator in which Guy Ritchie film of 2019?	4 Points
5	In what 2012 epic science fiction film did he have several roles across different plots?	5 Points
6	Who starred as his love interest in 'Music and Lyrics'?	6 Points
7	In what spy film from 2015 did he play a high-ranking MI6 agent?	7 Points
8	In what 1996 movie did he star as a doctor who uncovers illegal medical experiments?	8 Points
9	What film does Will watch on his own on Christmas Day in 'About a Boy'?	9 Points
10	In 'Did You Hear About the Morgans?', in what US state did Hugh and his wife go into hiding?	10 Points

9. Dawson's Creek Actors

1	In what 1997 horror sequel did Joshua Jackson have a small role as one of Jamie Kennedy's classmates?	**1 Point**
2	Name the musical film in which Michelle Williams played the wife of P.T. Barnum.	**2 Points**
3	In what film did Katie Holmes appear as the wife of Colin Farrell?	**3 Points**
4	In what film does Joshua Jackson appear as himself learning to play poker?	**4 Points**
5	In the romantic drama 'Blue Valentine', alongside whom did Michelle Williams star?	**5 Points**
6	In what 1999 comedy sports drama did James Van Der Beek star?	**6 Points**
7	What is the name of Michelle Williams' character in 'Manchester by the Sea'?	**7 Points**
8	In what critically-panned film about gambling, starring Bruce Willis and Rebecca Hall, did Joshua Jackson also star?	**8 Points**
9	Katie Holmes appeared in the film 'Woman in Gold', about what real-life woman trying to reclaim a famous painting?	**9 Points**
10	In 'Suite Francaise', who played the German soldier for whom Michelle Williams develops feelings?	**10 Points**

10. Magic

1	What is the prequel to the Harry Potter series, released in 2016?	1 Point
2	In which Massachusetts town is 'Hocus Pocus' set?	2 Points
3	The 2010 film 'The Sorcerer's Apprentice' is named after a segment in which film?	3 Points
4	Which two British comedians starred in the 2007 film 'The Magicians'?	4 Points
5	What do the magicians call themselves in 'Now You See Me'?	5 Points
6	In 'The Prestige', as whom does David Bowie appear?	6 Points
7	What is the source of Glinda's magic in 'Oz the Great and Powerful'?	7 Points
8	Who directed, produced and wrote 'Bewitched', based on the TV series?	8 Points
9	In which city is 'The Illusionist' set?	9 Points
10	What is the name of the deity worshipped by the girls in 'The Craft'?	10 Points

11. 1992

1	Steven Seagal played an ex Navy SEAL protecting a battleship in which action film?	**1 Point**
2	Paul Verhoeven directed which erotic thriller starring Michael Douglas and Sharon Stone?	**2 Points**
3	What breed of dog is Beethoven?	**3 Points**
4	In what Illinois city is 'Wayne's World' set?	**4 Points**
5	In which film does Jack Nicholson tell Tom Cruise "You can't handle the truth"?	**5 Points**
6	What thriller starred Annabella Sciorra and Rebecca de Mornay?	**6 Points**
7	Which character sells the magical potion in 'Death Becomes Her'?	**7 Points**
8	Who played the villain Cosmo in 'Sneakers'?	**8 Points**
9	What is the Las Vegas stage name of Whoopi Goldberg's character in 'Sister Act'?	**9 Points**
10	In 'My Cousin Vinny' what "confession" does Bill Gambino make?	**10 Points**

12. James McAvoy Movies

1	In 'Starter for 10', McAvoy was caught cheating on what TV show?	1 Point
2	What role did he play in 'The Chronicles of Narnia: The Lion, the Witch and the Wardrobe'?	2 Points
3	In 'Wanted', what does his character find out his father did for a living?	3 Points
4	Where is the setting for 'Filth', in which he plays a corrupt policeman?	4 Points
5	In which horror sequel does he play the grown-up character Bill?	5 Points
6	What was the first Marvel film in which he starred?	6 Points
7	In which sports film did he have an early role, appearing as the brother of Paul Bettany's character?	7 Points
8	What is his job in 'Atomic Blonde'?	8 Points
9	In what 2013 film did he star alongside Mark Strong?	9 Points
10	How many different personalities does his character have in 'Split'?	10 Points

13. Anagrams 1990s

1 point for each film identified

1	2	3
DANGER REC	ZONED BOTH HOY	BEREFT AFTER HO HID

4	5	6
HOWDY TO VIPER MANIA	TAG A REST	ALL RANKERS ROB UNTIL

7	8	9
ROBO MANGE	CHANGE YET GRIM	VIEW TITCH RUBS SELF

10
FOUNDER THIS MOLE RADA

14. Jurassic Park Movies

1	Who directed 'Jurassic Park'?	1 Point

2	'The Lost World' ends in which American city?	2 Points

3	Which actor reprised his role as Dr. Henry Wu in the 'Jurassic World' films?	3 Points

4	What are the full names of the characters played by Sam Neill and Laura Dern?	4 Points

5	Which dinosaurs stampede like a "flock of birds" in 'Jurassic Park'?	5 Points

6	Where does John Hammond say he wishes he'd located the park, as the storm is approaching in 'Jurassic Park'?	6 Points

7	What is the name of the new dinosaur created in 'Jurassic World: Fallen Kingdom' which at one point pretends to be asleep?	7 Points

8	In 'Jurassic World', what are the names of the four velociraptors trained by Owen Grady?	8 Points

9	Dennis Nedry attempts to smuggle dinosaur DNA out of Jurassic Park in what branded container?	9 Points

10	In 'Jurassic Park 3', what is the name of William H Macy's store, for which the satellite phone plays the jingle?	10 Points

15. Leonardo DiCaprio Movies

1	In which 1996 film, based on a Shakespeare play, did DiCaprio star?	**1 Point**
2	Who wrote the novel on which 'The Beach' was based?	**2 Points**
3	In 'Gangs of New York', his character had what name, the same as a European city?	**3 Points**
4	He plays the mentally impaired brother of Johnny Depp's character in which 1993 drama?	**4 Points**
5	What is his character's totem in 'Inception'?	**5 Points**
6	Who directed 'Shutter Island'?	**6 Points**
7	Who plays fisherman Solomon Vandy in 'Blood Diamond', helping DiCaprio recover a priceless diamond?	**7 Points**
8	Name the four films for which he has been nominated for the Best Actor Oscar without success.	**8 Points**
9	'The Man in the Iron Mask' was set during the reign of which French King?	**9 Points**
10	In 'Body of Lies', what does Leo take for dessert when he visits the nurse's home for dinner?	**10 Points**

16. 1993

1	In what film does Robin Williams dress up as a nanny?	**1 Point**

2	What is the value of the 'Indecent Proposal' in the film of the same name?	**2 Points**

3	Who does Harrison Ford play in 'The Fugitive'?	**3 Points**

4	What song does Phil repeatedly hear on waking up in 'Groundhog Day'?	**4 Points**

5	Who plays the police detective chasing Michael Douglas in 'Falling Down'?	**5 Points**

6	In 'Sleepless in Seattle', where does Annie live?	**6 Points**

7	Who directed 'Alive', about the survivors of a plane crash in the Andes?	**7 Points**

8	In which city is 'So I Married an Axe Murderer' set?	**8 Points**

9	At the end of 'In the Line of Fire', what landmark do Frank and Lily visit?	**9 Points**

10	In 'Demolition Man' what password does Wesley Snipes give, to be released from his chains in prison?	**10 Points**

17. Cameron Diaz Movies

1	Diaz voices Princess Fiona in what series of films?	**1 Point**
2	Her first role was as Tina in which film?	**2 Points**
3	In 'The Holiday', what city does her character swap for London?	**3 Points**
4	Which Angel did she play in 'Charlie's Angels'?	**4 Points**
5	Name the two films in which she has starred with Tom Cruise.	**5 Points**
6	In what early Danny Boyle film did she star alongside Ewan McGregor?	**6 Points**
7	In 'Very Bad Things', who played her husband?	**7 Points**
8	In 'There's Something About Mary', Pat Healy asks Mary for some change because he only has what?	**8 Points**
9	Which actor is the object of affection for the women in 'The Other Woman'?	**9 Points**
10	What causes her to mess up her MTV audition in 'In Her Shoes'?	**10 Points**

1 point for each winner named

Name the 10 most recent Best Actor Oscar Winners (for films from 2010 to 2019)

19. Mark Wahlberg Movies

1	In what 2003 remake featuring Minis does Wahlberg play Charlie Croker?	**1 Point**
2	In which action franchise did he first appear in 2014?	**2 Points**
3	In what film did he play Dirk Diggler?	**3 Points**
4	'Patriots Day' depicted the events at the marathon of which city?	**4 Points**
5	In 'Three Kings', Wahlberg's captor accuses Americans of hating which celebrity?	**5 Points**
6	In 'Lone Survivor', in which mountain range do his team die?	**6 Points**
7	Who is kidnapped in the 2017 film 'All the Money in the World'?	**7 Points**
8	What is the name of Ted's wife in 'Ted 2'?	**8 Points**
9	What song is played when Wahlberg comes down the airport escalator in 'Daddy's Home'?	**9 Points**
10	In 'Invincible', which real life American football player does Mark play?	**10 Points**

20. Cryptic Clues #1

1 point for each film identified

1	2	3
↑	Steve John Phil Jane	WHAT LIES

4	5	6
W R O A R	Short ↗ Short	hero hero hero hero hero **HERO**

7	8	9
bowie carving [ ] hunting	♀♀♀♀	A M 3 2 6 9

10
1/4 F

21. 1994

1	Which Disney film featured Simba, Mufasa and Scar?	**1 Point**
2	Who played the pregnant man in 'Junior'?	**2 Points**
3	Who sang the theme song for 'The Flintstones'?	**3 Points**
4	Who died during the filming of 'The Crow'?	**4 Points**
5	Which future Oscar winner made her film debut in 'Leon'?	**5 Points**
6	In 'Speed', the bus will blow up if it goes below how many miles per hour?	**6 Points**
7	What is the name of the film in which Kathleen Turner played a serial killer?	**7 Points**
8	The thriller 'Disclosure' was based on a novel by whom?	**8 Points**
9	How much does Nicolas Cage's cop give to Bridget Fonda's waitress when he wins the lottery in 'It Could Happen to You'?	**9 Points**
10	Which game show features in the film 'Quiz Show'?	**10 Points**

22. Pixar

1	What insect was Flik in 'A Bug's Life'?	**1 Point**

2	What film, set in the Scottish highlands, is about a Princess who has good archery skills?	**2 Points**

3	In what city was 'Monsters Inc.' set?	**3 Points**

4	In what film was a 12 year-old boy transported to the Land of the Dead?	**4 Points**

5	What does 'WALL-E' stand for?	**5 Points**

6	What is the surname of the superhero family in 'The Incredibles'?	**6 Points**

7	What was the name of 'The Good Dinosaur'?	**7 Points**

8	What was the name of Riley's imaginary friend in 'Inside Out'?	**8 Points**

9	Name the restaurant in 'Ratatouille'.	**9 Points**

10	What sort of fish is Dory in 'Finding Dory'?	**10 Points**

23. Harrison Ford Movies

1	What was the 4th installment of the Indiana Jones franchise, released in 2008?	1 Point
2	In 'Patriot Games', who starred as Sean Miller who was hell bent on revenge throughout the film?	2 Points
3	In what 1991 film does Ford's character suffer amnesia after being shot?	3 Points
4	In 'The Devil's Own', the man who comes to live with his character's family is part of what organisation?	4 Points
5	In 'Random Hearts', how does his wife die?	5 Points
6	In 'Morning Glory', who stars as his co-anchor on the morning TV show Daybreak?	6 Points
7	In what film, also starring Paul Bettany, did he play a chief of security at a bank?	7 Points
8	In '42' he played the real-life person Branch Rickey, who signed which Major League Baseball player?	8 Points
9	At the end of 'Clear and Present Danger', in which country does a rescue of US soldiers take place led by Jack Ryan?	9 Points
10	In 'Presumed Innocent', who played his wife who committed the crime of which he was accused?	10 Points

24. Romcoms

1	Complete the name of the Reese Witherspoon film: 'Sweet Home...'?	1 Point
2	How many days of summer were in the 2009 film?	2 Points
3	Who played the lead role in '40 Days and 40 Nights'?	3 Points
4	What film saw Steve Carrell start dating again after splitting from his wife, played by Julianne Moore?	4 Points
5	What is the name of Reese Witherspoon's character in 'Legally Blonde'?	5 Points
6	Upon which Shakespeare play was '10 Things I Hate About You' loosely based?	6 Points
7	Name the 2013 film, starring Nicholas Hoult, in which a zombie falls in love.	7 Points
8	In 'While You Were Sleeping', where does Sandra Bullock work?	8 Points
9	In 'Trainwreck', what TV show does Lebron James want Aaron to watch with him?	9 Points
10	Name the 1999 film starring Jennifer Aniston as a career woman who hires Jay Mohr to be her fiancé.	10 Points

25. Animals #1

1	What is the name of the lion in 'The Chronicles of Narnia'?	1 Point

2	What do Matt Damon and his family buy in the 2011 film?	2 Points

3	In 'Marley and Me', what breed of dog is Marley?	3 Points

4	In 'The Rise of the Planet of the Apes', what is the name of the chimpanzee which Will takes home and raises?	4 Points

5	Who voiced 'The Fantastic Mr Fox' in 2009?	5 Points

6	What are the expensive pets that Deuce is hired to look after In 'Deuce Bigalow: Male Gigalo'?	6 Points

7	What film sees Liam Neeson hunted by wolves?	7 Points

8	In 'Life of Pi', what does Pi name the tiger?	8 Points

9	What is the name of the mouse brought back to life in 'The Green Mile'?	9 Points

10	Which film starred Paul Walker trying to rescue his dogs from the Antarctic?	10 Points

26. 1995

1	Who was the friendly ghost?	**1 Point**

2	What movie was based on a TV show from the 1970s about a large family?	**2 Points**

3	What film starred Hugh Grant and Julianne Moore as expecting parents?	**3 Points**

4	Which film was Danny Boyle's directorial debut?	**4 Points**

5	In which year were the events depicted in 'Apollo 13'?	**5 Points**

6	In 'Get Shorty', what borrowed item causes clashes between Palmer and Barboni?	**6 Points**

7	From what phobia did Sigourney Weaver suffer in 'Copycat'?	**7 Points**

8	What is the name of the talking gorilla in 'Congo'?	**8 Points**

9	What is the name of the town at the centre of 'Outbreak', which the army plan to bomb at the end of the film?	**9 Points**

10	Which song features in the opening scene of 'Die Hard with a Vengeance', when a department store is blown up?	**10 Points**

27. Name the Movie From the Tagline #1

1	Check in. Unpack. Relax. Take a shower.	**1 Point**
2	Jason is ready for adulthood. His grandpa isn't.	**2 Points**
3	When your Dad's an undertaker, your Mom's in heaven, and your Grandma's got a screw loose...it's good to have a friend who understands you. Even if he is a boy.	**3 Points**
4	A game for those who seek to find a way to leave their world behind.	**4 Points**
5	You won't believe your eye.	**5 Points**
6	Whoever wins, we lose.	**6 Points**
7	The last man on Earth is not alone.	**7 Points**
8	His story will touch you, even if he can't.	**8 Points**
9	An adventure as big as life itself.	**9 Points**
10	Here they go again. Only faster. And tougher.	**10 Points**

28. Westerns

1	What film sequel starring Emilio Estevez and Kiefer Sutherland was about Billy the Kid?	**1 Point**
2	What Western / sci-fi film from 2011 was directed by Jon Favreau?	**2 Points**
3	In 'City Slickers', what gift experience do Phil and Ed give Mitch?	**3 Points**
4	Who starred as the title character in 1994's 'Wyatt Earp'?	**4 Points**
5	What is Russell Crowe's occupation in 'The Quick and the Dead'?	**5 Points**
6	What Western starred Madeleine Stowe, Andie MacDowell and Drew Barrymore?	**6 Points**
7	Which character hires the eponymous gang in 2016's 'The Magnificent Seven'?	**7 Points**
8	In what town do Boss and Charley settle down in 'Open Range'?	**8 Points**
9	In 'The Horse Whisperer', what is the name of the horse to which Robert Redford's character "whispers"?	**9 Points**
10	In 'Tombstone', what are Doc Holliday's dying words?	**10 Points**

29. Kate Winslet Movies

1	'Finding Neverland' was about the life of which author?	**1 Point**
2	What is the full name of the character Winslet and Judi Dench both played in 'Iris'?	**2 Points**
3	In what animated film does she voice the love interest of a pet rat who has been discarded down the toilet?	**3 Points**
4	In which film from 2008 did she play a woman who can't read?	**4 Points**
5	Which 2008 film saw her appear alongside Leonardo DiCaprio again following their performances in 'Titanic'?	**5 Points**
6	In which country was 'The Dressmaker' set?	**6 Points**
7	What 2016 drama with an ensemble cast, including Will Smith, was panned by critics?	**7 Points**
8	In which state does the plane come down, in 'The Mountain Between Us'?	**8 Points**
9	Who did she star alongside in the 2013 drama film 'Labor Day'?	**9 Points**
10	Where does her character work in 'Contagion'?	**10 Points**

30. Space

1	Who did Ryan Gosling star as in 'First Man'?	**1 Point**

2	What 2014 film saw Matthew McConaughey play an explorer looking for a new world?	**2 Points**

3	Which film of the 'Alien' franchise was released in 1997?	**3 Points**

4	In 'The Martian', what food did Mark Watney manage to grow?	**4 Points**

5	Who directed 'Gravity'?	**5 Points**

6	What did a New York school choose as the name for the new lifeform in 'Life'?	**6 Points**

7	What 2009 film saw Ben Foster and Dennis Quaid as astronauts woken up mid-hypersleep?	**7 Points**

8	From which star system does the contact come from in 1997's 'Contact'?	**8 Points**

9	What was the name of the ship sent to rescue the 'Event Horizon'?	**9 Points**

10	What nicknames were given to the first two aliens we meet in 'Arrival'?	**10 Points**

31. 1996

1	How many dalmations feature in the name of the Disney film?	1 Point

2	Which film, based on a Roald Dahl book, starred the child actress Mara Wilson as the title character?	2 Points

3	What does Tom Cruise shout down the phone in 'Jerry Maguire'?	3 Points

4	The last dragon and a dragonslayer must team up in which fantasy film starring Dennis Quaid?	4 Points

5	How much money do the kidnappers ask for in 'Ransom'?	5 Points

6	Which Renny Harlin directed film sees Geena Davis as a spy with amnesia?	6 Points

7	What untimely end does Steve Buscemi's character meet in 'Fargo'?	7 Points

8	Quentin Tarantino wrote but didn't direct which horror film?	8 Points

9	In 'The Truth About Cats and Dogs', what is the job of Abby, played by Janeane Garofalo?	9 Points

10	In 'The English Patient', what is the patient's only posession?	10 Points

32. Thrillers #1

1	In what 2002 film did Kevin Bacon turn himself invisible?	**1 Point**
2	Who starred as the title character in 2010's 'Salt'?	**2 Points**
3	In the 1992 film 'Unlawful Entry', who played the policeman stalking a married couple?	**3 Points**
4	Into which city is the train travelling in 'Source Code'?	**4 Points**
5	Name the political thriller of 2011 directed by and starring George Clooney, also featuring Ryan Gosling?	**5 Points**
6	In what 1990 film did Michael Keaton play a bad tenant of Melanie Griffith?	**6 Points**
7	In what country was the action thriller 'The Kingdom' set?	**7 Points**
8	'Children of Men' was based on a 1992 novel by which crime writer?	**8 Points**
9	In 'Single White Female', how does Buddy the golden retriever puppy die?	**9 Points**
10	In 'The Town', where do the group make their final robbery?	**10 Points**

33. Name the Movie From the Quote #1

1	"I wish I knew how to quit you."	**1 Point**
2	"They may take our lives, but they'll never take our freedom!"	**2 Points**
3	"I have nipples Greg. Could you milk me?"	**3 Points**
4	"No. You must believe me. it was a horseman, a dead one. Headless."	**4 Points**
5	"Make it quick, because my horse is getting tired"	**5 Points**
6	"I'm going to steal the Declaration of Independence"	**6 Points**
7	"You is kind. You is smart. You is important."	**7 Points**
8	"I found a cure for the plague of the 20th century, and now I've lost it."	**8 Points**
9	"I'm just one stomach flu away from my goal weight"	**9 Points**
10	"I saw a man strangle a human being... well, an accountant anyway"	**10 Points**

34. Arnie Movies

1	Which film from 2010, which launched a franchise about a team of mercenaries, featured Arnie in an uncredited role?	1 Point
2	In which Christmas film does he play a dad trying to get a toy for his son?	2 Points
3	He plays Mr Freeze in which Batman film?	3 Points
4	In what film does he play an ex-copy trying to stop Satan in New York?	4 Points
5	In the film 'Maggie', what is wrong with his daughter?	5 Points
6	He starred as Quaid in what Philip K. Dick adaptation?	6 Points
7	Who played his boss in 'Eraser'?	7 Points
8	In 'Last Action Hero', who is his character in the films within the film?	8 Points
9	Who played his best friend in 'The 6th Day'?	9 Points
10	In 'Terminator: Dark Fate', what human name does the terminator take?	10 Points

35. Where in the World..... #1

1	...did Brad Pitt spend seven years?	**1 Point**
2	...did Beavis and Butthead "do"?	**2 Points**
3	...is P.L. Travers' childhood home in 'Saving Mr Banks'?	**3 Points**
4	...did Sully land his plane in the 'miracle' of the 2016 film?	**4 Points**
5	...does Blake Lively go surfing in 'The Shallows'?	**5 Points**
6	...was the hotel in a 2004 film starring Don Cheadle?	**6 Points**
7	...was 'The Wolverine' mostly set?	**7 Points**
8	...was Eddie Murphy's fictional kingdom in 'Coming to America'?	**8 Points**
9	...does Russell Crowe go looking for his three missing sons in 'The Water Diviner'?	**9 Points**
10	...is Daniel Radcliffe lost in 2017's 'Jungle'?	**10 Points**

36. 1997

1	Mike Myers starred as which 'International Man of Mystery'?	1 Point
2	Who played the President in 'Air Force One'?	2 Points
3	In 'The Full Monty', what song do the men start dancing to at the Job Centre?	3 Points
4	Which two actors shared a famous kiss in 'In & Out'?	4 Points
5	Which two music stars featured in 'Anaconda'?	5 Points
6	In what satirical sci-fi action film is there an interstellar war between humankind and an insectoid species known as "Arachnids"?	6 Points
7	In what film is a soldier killed, then resurrected as a reluctant leader of the devil's army?	7 Points
8	What do Romy and Michelle claim to have invented in 'Romy and Michelle's High School Reunion'?	8 Points
9	What romantic comedy won Best Actor and Actress Oscars for its leads?	9 Points
10	At which airport do the inmates plan to swap planes in 'Con Air'?	10 Points

37. Three Words #1

1 point for each film identified

1	2	3
dolphin Birdsville poo	just sack Pat	Chicago brothers arson

4	5	6
wings Aurora spindle	time Kathmandu surgeon	Christmas penguin Shreck

7	8	9
plane terrorist Snipes	fishing IRS Ariel	satellite Chip stutter

10
fraternity streaking Blue

38. Comedies #1

1	Who starred with Chris Tucker in the 'Rush Hour' films?	**1 Point**
2	What sport did Happy Gilmore take up?	**2 Points**
3	By what name was Jeff Bridge's character known in 'The Big Lebowski'?	**3 Points**
4	What character did Charlie Sheen play in the 'Hot Shots' films?	**4 Points**
5	In 'Mean Girls', Cady tries to infiltrate a group of popular girls known as what?	**5 Points**
6	Which two actors played the lead roles in 'Superbad'?	**6 Points**
7	Richard Griffiths appeared as Dr Albert Meinheimer in which 1991 film?	**7 Points**
8	Which rap star appeared in 'Spy'?	**8 Points**
9	What is the name of White Goodman's dodgeball team in 'DodgeBall: A True Underdog Story'?	**9 Points**
10	In 'Step Brothers', why is Dale upset with the amount of money his father leaves him for food?	**10 Points**

39. Animation #1

1	Russell Brand voiced the Easter Bunny in which 2011 film?	1 Point

2	Which cartoon character appeared on the poster for 'Space Jam'?	2 Points

3	In what film does Danny DeVito voice the main character, a mystical orange furry creature?	3 Points

4	The three main characters in 'Ice Age' are a woolly mammoth, a ground sloth and what other animal?	4 Points

5	In 'Sausage Party', who voices the main character, a sausage named 'Frank'?	5 Points

6	Where is the film 'Lilo & Stitch' set?	6 Points

7	What is the name of the race that Dusty enters in 'Planes'?	7 Points

8	What 2006 movie told the story of a bear, deer and other animals teaming up to defeat hunters?	8 Points

9	In 'Puss in Boots', what is the name of Puss' hometown that he ultimately saves?	9 Points

10	In 'The Secret Life of Pets', what is the name of the group of pets who live in the sewers?	10 Points

40. Bruce Willis Movies

1	How many monkeys are in the name of the 1995 sci-fi film in which Willis starred?	**1 Point**
2	'The Jackal' was a remake of which film from 1973?	**2 Points**
3	He starred as a retired spy in which film from 2010, and its sequel in 2013?	**3 Points**
4	In what 1991 action film did he star alongside Damon Wayans?	**4 Points**
5	In which Disney film does his character meet his younger self?	**5 Points**
6	Who directed the 2012 coming-of-age film 'Moonrise Kingdom', in which he starred as Captain Sharp?	**6 Points**
7	In 'Over the Hedge', he voices the main character RJ, who is what sort of animal?	**7 Points**
8	In what 1990 black comedy film did he appear alongside Tom Hanks and Melanie Griffith?	**8 Points**
9	In Lucky Number Slevin, what is the name of the double bluff which he tells the story of?	**9 Points**
10	In 'Live Free or Die Hard', when Matt says to John McClane "You just killed a car with a helicopter", what does John reply?	**10 Points**

41. 1998

1	What was the name of the film starring the Spice Girls?	**1 Point**
2	The fourth installment of which Mel Gibson and Danny Glover franchise was released in this year?	**2 Points**
3	Which two films were about a meteor heading for Earth?	**3 Points**
4	Who directed the crime comedy 'Out of Sight'?	**4 Points**
5	In what film did Tommy Lee Jones reprise his role as Sam Gerrard?	**5 Points**
6	The boy who Bruce Willis protects in 'Mercury Rising' has what condition?	**6 Points**
7	Where does 'Godzilla' lay its eggs?	**7 Points**
8	'Return to Paradise' saw Anne Heche asking Vince Vaughn and David Conrad to go back to which country?	**8 Points**
9	Which song does Robbie sing to Julia on the airplane at the end of 'The Wedding Singer'?	**9 Points**
10	What code name does Gene Hackman use in 'Enemy of the State'?	**10 Points**

42. News

1	Complete the movie title: 'Anchorman: The Legend of...'?	**1 Point**
2	Who starred as Evan who was promoted above Bruce to news anchorman in 'Bruce Almighty'?	**2 Points**
3	'Zodiac' from 2007 tells the story of reporters in which city trying to track down a serial killer?	**3 Points**
4	What 2016 film starred George Clooney as a TV financial expert?	**4 Points**
5	'Bombshell' from 2019 was about women setting out to expose sexual harrassment by the CEO of which news channel?	**5 Points**
6	Which newspaper broke the story in 'Spotlight'?	**6 Points**
7	In 'Shaun of the Dead', which real news presenter is shown on TV saying 'the assailants can be stopped by removing the head or destroying the brain'?	**7 Points**
8	What was the 2005 film, set in 1953, about a broadcast journalist trying to bring down a senator in the USA?	**8 Points**
9	Name the real people portrayed by Meryl Streep and Tom Hanks in 'The Post'.	**9 Points**
10	What is the name of the news anchor who Benji impersonates at the start of 'Mission: Impossible - Fallout'?	**10 Points**

43. Sport #1

1	What film was about the Jamaican bobsleigh team?	**1 Point**

2	The film 'Bring It On' focuses on what?	**2 Points**

3	For what 2009 film did Sandra Bullock win an Oscar, playing a woman who adopts a future NFL player?	**3 Points**

4	'The Fan' sees Robert De Niro stalk a star of which sport?	**4 Points**

5	Name the sports team at the centre of 'Any Given Sunday'.	**5 Points**

6	What 1994 documentary, about high school basketball players in Chicago, received critical acclaim?	**6 Points**

7	What was the 2017 biographical drama about an American figure skater?	**7 Points**

8	What film is about the promising sportsman Jim Carroll, who develops an addiction to heroin?	**8 Points**

9	In what film did Kevin Costner star as the General Manager of the Cleveland Browns?	**9 Points**

10	A poem by whom inspired the title of a 2009 film about the Rugby World Cup and post-apartheid South Africa?	**10 Points**

44. Travel

1	Which 'Breaking Bad' actor starred in the 2014 film 'Need for Speed'?	**1 Point**
2	What is Ryan Gosling's day job in 'Drive'?	**2 Points**
3	What horror film from 2005 was about a woman taking an overnight flight?	**3 Points**
4	Who starred as Baby in 'Baby Driver'?	**4 Points**
5	In 2006's 'Cars', Paul Newman voiced which character?	**5 Points**
6	What 2012 film saw Barbra Streisand and Seth Rogen play a mother and son on a road trip?	**6 Points**
7	In the film 'RV' where do Robin Williams and his family go on holiday?	**7 Points**
8	What is Liam Neeson's job in 'Non-Stop'?	**8 Points**
9	Where was Furiosa taking Immortan Joe's wives in 'Mad Max: Fury Road'?	**9 Points**
10	'Wild', starring Reese Witherspoon, was about which real-life person?	**10 Points**

45. Weather

1	What 1996 film was about a group of tornado chasers?	**1 Point**
2	Which Kevin Costner movie was set in the future when the polar ice cap has melted and most of Earth is covered by water?	**2 Points**
3	Who starred as 'The Weather Man' in the 2005 film?	**3 Points**
4	What 1998 film starred Morgan Freeman as a robber caught in a bad storm?	**4 Points**
5	In which New York building do the students take shelter in 'The Day After Tomorrow'?	**5 Points**
6	What horror movie from 2005, centred around an island town in Oregon, was a remake of a 1980 film?	**6 Points**
7	In '2012', what causes the Earth's core to heat up?	**7 Points**
8	In 'Percy Jackson and the Lightning Thief', who is Percy's father?	**8 Points**
9	Which 2017 film starred Jeremy Renner as a US Fish and Wildlife Service tracker?	**9 Points**
10	What is the name of the vessel in 'The Perfect Storm'?	**10 Points**

46. 1999

1	Matthew Broderick starred as which inspector in the title of the family film?	**1 Point**
2	Who starred in and sang the theme song to 'Wild Wild West'?	**2 Points**
3	Haley Joel Osment told Bruce Willis he could see dead people in which film?	**3 Points**
4	Which horror film, which cost just $60,000 to make, grossed over $240m worldwide?	**4 Points**
5	What black comedy focused on individuals working for a software company who are weary of their jobs?	**5 Points**
6	What distracts Keanu Reeves' character when he is receiving a tutorial from Laurence Fishburne in 'The Matrix'?	**6 Points**
7	In what film do a police officer and a bed-bound quadriplegic forensics expert try and solve a series of murders?	**7 Points**
8	Which female star of the TV shows 'Ally McBeal' and '30 Rock' also appeared in the movie 'Go'?	**8 Points**
9	What building was blown up at the end of 'Arlington Road'?	**9 Points**
10	What is the name of the high school where Drew Barrymore goes undercover in 'Never Been Kissed'?	**10 Points**

47. Name the Movie From the Featured Song #1

1	'City of Stars' by Ryan Gosling and Emma Stone	**1 Point**
2	'I Will Always Love You' by Whitney Houston	**2 Points**
3	'The Shoop Shoop Song (It's in His Kiss)' by Cher	**3 Points**
4	'Happy' by Pharrell Williams	**4 Points**
5	'I Don't Wanna Miss a Thing' by Aerosmith	**5 Points**
6	'Kiss From a Rose' by Seal	**6 Points**
7	'Jai Ho' by Sukhwinder Singh, Tanvi Shah, Mahalakshmi Iyer and Vijay Prakash	**7 Points**
8	'You Know My Name' by Chris Cornell	**8 Points**
9	'Bittersweet Symphony' by The Verve	**9 Points**
10	'Shy Guy' by Diana King	**10 Points**

48. Nicole Kidman Movies

1	As well as 'Days of Thunder' and 'Eyes Wide Shut', in which 1990s film did she appear alongside Tom Cruise?	**1 Point**
2	Who directed 'Eyes Wide Shut'?	**2 Points**
3	Who starred alongside her in 'The Interpreter'?	**3 Points**
4	She wore a prosthetic nose to appear in which 2002 film?	**4 Points**
5	On which island was 'The Others' set?	**5 Points**
6	What critically-panned remake in 2004 was based on an Ira Levin novel?	**6 Points**
7	'The Peacemaker', in which she starred with George Clooney, was the first film from which production label?	**7 Points**
8	In 'Cold Mountain', the titular mountain is part of what American range?	**8 Points**
9	Name the thriller from 1993 in which she starred with Bull Pullman and Alec Baldwin.	**9 Points**
10	In 1995's 'To Die For', who are the two future Oscar winners that played teenagers Kidman manipulates?	**10 Points**

49. Lord of the Rings

1	On whose books are the films based?	**1 Point**
2	In which country were the movies primarily shot?	**2 Points**
3	By what name was Gollum known before he was corrupted?	**3 Points**
4	Who appeared as Samwise Gamgee in all three films?	**4 Points**
5	Name the character who said "Nine companions. So be it. You shall be the fellowship of the ring."	**5 Points**
6	How many rings did Sauron give to the dwarves?	**6 Points**
7	What gift does Lady Galadriel give Gimli before the fellowship leaves Lothlorien?	**7 Points**
8	Who composed the music for the trilogy?	**8 Points**
9	Name the five wizards sent to help the people of Middle Earth.	**9 Points**
10	In what battle did Gorbag start a fight with the Cirith-Ungol?	**10 Points**

50. Drama #1

1	What film is about a lawyer who works out of a car instead of an office?	**1 Point**
2	In 'Murder in the First', at which prison is Henri Young incarcerated?	**2 Points**
3	Who starred as Matt King in 'The Descendants'?	**3 Points**
4	Which Oscar did 'Bridge of Spies' win?	**4 Points**
5	In 'Flight', what manoeuvre does the Captain make in order to stop the plane crashing?	**5 Points**
6	In what film from 1993 does Kevin Costner star as an escaped convict who befriends a young boy?	**6 Points**
7	In 'Philomena', which real-life journalist did Steve Coogan play?	**7 Points**
8	In 'Sommersby', what epic poem does Jack read to his sons, raising suspicions that he is not who he says he is?	**8 Points**
9	In 'The Pursuit of Happyness', Chris impresses his future boss by solving what puzzle?	**9 Points**
10	In 'Prisoners', Detective Loki tracks down a suspect and finds lots of crates, filled with what?	**10 Points**

51. 2000

1	Who "Must Die" in the title of the action film starring Jet Li?	1 Point
2	What famous question did Maximus ask of the crowd after defeating several enemies in 'Gladiator'?	2 Points
3	Who appeared as Riddick in 'Pitch Black'?	3 Points
4	Which Coen Brothers directed film was based on Homer's The Odyssey?	4 Points
5	In which film does Jennifer Lopez enter the mind of a serial killer?	5 Points
6	In 'What Women Want', what song was Mel Gibson listening to when he was electrocuted?	6 Points
7	Who played the lead character sent to rehab In '28 Days'?	7 Points
8	Against which company did 'Erin Brockovich' fight?	8 Points
9	What was the flight number and destination of the doomed flight in 'Final Destination'?	9 Points
10	What was the full name of Charlie's second personality in 'Me, Myself & Irene'?	10 Points

52. Adam Sandler Movies

1	In 'Uncut Gems' from 2019, what sort of store did Sandler own?	**1 Point**
2	Who played his therapist in 'Anger Management'?	**2 Points**
3	Which actor played his husband in 'I Now Pronounce You Chuck and Larry'?	**3 Points**
4	In 'You Don't Mess with the Zohan', what job does his character dream of doing?	**4 Points**
5	In which film does David Hasselhoff play his boss?	**5 Points**
6	In which animated film does he voice Count Dracula?	**6 Points**
7	'Mr Deeds' is a remake of which 1936 film?	**7 Points**
8	Over which weekend do the men reunite in 'Grown Ups'?	**8 Points**
9	What does the boy Julian decide to rename himself in 'Big Daddy'?	**9 Points**
10	He ends up playing American football for which college in 'The Water Boy'?	**10 Points**

53. These Movies All Have "American" in the Title

1	What 1999 film was about four teenage boys trying to lose their virginity on prom night?	**1 Point**
2	George Clooney played a hitman in which film of 2010?	**2 Points**
3	Edward Norton and Edward Furlong starred in which 1998 film about a former neo-Nazi?	**3 Points**
4	Denzel Washington and Russell Crowe starred in which Ridley Scott directed crime film from 2007?	**4 Points**
5	What film from 2019 documented a Chinese firm taking over an abandoned General Motors plant?	**5 Points**
6	Michael Douglas tries to date a lobbyist played by Annette Bening in which film?	**6 Points**
7	What is the 2015 film starring Jessie Eisenberg as a stoner turned government agent?	**7 Points**
8	Tom Cruise starred in which film, inspired by the life of Barry Seal?	**8 Points**
9	Ewan McGregor and Jennifer Connelly played a married couple at the heart of what film from 2016?	**9 Points**
10	The watermark feature of Paul Allen's business card astounded the main character in which film?	**10 Points**

54. Horror #1

1	What 1990 film about giant worms starred Kevin Bacon?	**1 Point**
2	Which title character was summoned when his name was said into a mirror five times?	**2 Points**
3	In which country was 'Wolf Creek' set?	**3 Points**
4	After watching the video in 'The Ring', how many days does the viewer have left to live?	**4 Points**
5	Which socialite had a small part in 'House of Wax'?	**5 Points**
6	Which character is nicknamed Jigsaw, in the 'Saw' films?	**6 Points**
7	Which actor played the gang leader in 'Eden Lake'?	**7 Points**
8	Who starred as paranormal investigators in 'The Conjuring'?	**8 Points**
9	What does the number plate say on The Creeper's truck in 'Jeepers Creepers'?	**9 Points**
10	In 'The Cabin in the Woods', which monster did Bradley Whitford's character bet on in the sweepstake?	**10 Points**

55. Friends Actors

1	Which series of horror films saw Courtney Cox play Gale Weathers?	1 Point

2	How old did Matthew Perry's character become again in the 2009 film?	2 Points

3	In which film does Matt LeBlanc have a cameo as an action star boyfriend of one of the main characters?	3 Points

4	David Schwimmer plays Anne Heche's boyfriend in which film, also starring Harrison Ford?	4 Points

5	In which film does Jennifer Aniston's daughter enter a beauty pageant?	5 Points

6	Lisa Kudrow played the Dean in which comedy starring Zac Efron?	6 Points

7	In which Simon Pegg film does David Schwimmer have an uncredited cameo as a man handing a marathon runner a beer?	7 Points

8	In the film 'Derailed', who plays Jennifer Aniston's boyfriend?	8 Points

9	In what film, about a robbery in Las Vegas, did Courtney Cox star alongside Kurt Russell, Christian Slater and Kevin Costner?	9 Points

10	What was the name of Matt LeBlanc's character in 'Lost in Space'?	10 Points

56. 2001

1	Paul Walker and Vin Diesel starred in which film, the first of a successful franchise?	1 Point
2	Brendan Fraser, Rachel Weisz and John Hannah reprised their roles in which sequel?	2 Points
3	Which psychological thriller starred Guy Pearce?	3 Points
4	Who directed the musical film 'Moulin Rouge'?	4 Points
5	Brad Pitt and Julia Roberts starred together in which comedy film?	5 Points
6	What was the theme song to the film 'Pearl Harbour'?	6 Points
7	Jim Broadbent won a Best Supporting Actor Oscar for his role in which film from this year?	7 Points
8	In the film 'Blow', Johnny Depp played which famous drug smuggler?	8 Points
9	In 'Planet of the Apes', who played General Thade, the chimpanzee military commander?	9 Points
10	In 'One Night at McCool's', what was the name of Liv Tyler's character?	10 Points

57. Action #1

1	Who starred as 'The Accountant' in the 2016 film?	**1 Point**
2	In the 2005 action film, the 'Four Brothers' are avenging the death of whom?	**2 Points**
3	Who reprised his role as Kevin Flynn in 'Tron: Legacy'?	**3 Points**
4	What is Kurt Russell's character called in 'Escape from L.A.'?	**4 Points**
5	In what film does Goldie Hawn's character discover her ex is an FBI informant under witness protection?	**5 Points**
6	On which island is the climactic battle in 'X-Men'?	**6 Points**
7	What action adventure from 2005, starring Matthew McConaughey and Penelope Cruz, was a box office bomb?	**7 Points**
8	Name the villain played by Benedict Cumberbatch in 'Star Trek Into Darkness'?	**8 Points**
9	How was the Kraken defeated in 'Clash of the Titans'?	**9 Points**
10	What was the name of the submarine in 'Crimson Tide'?	**10 Points**

58. Book Adaptations

1	What 1996 Danny Boyle film about the Edinburgh drug scene was based on an Irvine Welsh book?	1 Point
2	What film starring Brad Pitt and Edward Norton is based on a book by Chuck Palahniuk?	2 Points
3	'Journey to the Center of the Earth' from 2008 was an adaptation of whose book?	3 Points
4	What was the full name of the Stephen King book upon which 'The Shawshank Redemption' was based'?	4 Points
5	Which Tom Hanks movie was based on a book by Winston Groom?	5 Points
6	What biographical black comedy crime film from 2018 was based on a memoir by Ron Stallworth?	6 Points
7	What classic noir novel from James Ellroy was turned into a 1997 film?	7 Points
8	What Iranian film from 2007, based on a novel, was nominated for the Best Animated Picture Oscar?	8 Points
9	'Bridge to Terabithia' was based on the novel of the same name by which Chinese-born American writer?	9 Points
10	Who wrote the 1968 novel 'True Grit', on which the 2010 film was based?	10 Points

59. Food

1	What were fried and green in the title of a 1991 film?	**1 Point**
2	Which 2005 film from Tim Burton was a remake of a 1971 classic, and based on a Roald Dahl book?	**2 Points**
3	Who stars as Harvey Milk in the 2008 biopic?	**3 Points**
4	In the film 'Hannibal', what food does Ray Liotta say smells good?	**4 Points**
5	What does 'The Pale Man' eat in 'Pan's Labyrinth'?	**5 Points**
6	Which 2009 film, about a blogger cooking all of the recipes in one book, stars Meryl Streep and Amy Adams?	**6 Points**
7	What contest is threatened by the Were-Rabbit in the 2005 Wallace and Gromit film?	**7 Points**
8	What live animal is eaten in the original 'Oldboy'?	**8 Points**
9	How many tiers did the wedding cake have in 'Crazy Rich Asians'?	**9 Points**
10	What three things does Mark help Bridget cook for her birthday dinner in 'Bridget Jones' Diary'?	**10 Points**

60. Film Scores / Soundtrack - Name the Composer

1	Jurassic Park	**1 Point**

2	The Piano	**2 Points**

3	Tarzan	**3 Points**

4	Gladiator	**4 Points**

5	Avatar	**5 Points**

6	Mission: Impossible	**6 Points**

7	Million Dollar Baby	**7 Points**

8	About a Boy	**8 Points**

9	The Hateful Eight	**9 Points**

10	There Will be Blood	**10 Points**

61. 2002

1	In 'Stuart Little 2', Michael J. Fox reprised his role voicing what sort of animal?	**1 Point**
2	In 'K19: The Widowmaker', what is K19?	**2 Points**
3	In what film does the main character Toula work at her parents' Greek restaurant 'Dancing Zorba's'?	**3 Points**
4	In an early film role, who played Jodie Foster's daughter in 'Panic Room'?	**4 Points**
5	Who was nominated for an Oscar for their performance in 'Unfaithful'?	**5 Points**
6	What musical film won the Best Picture Oscar?	**6 Points**
7	Who directed Al Pacino, Robin Williams and Hilary Swank in 'Insomnia'?	**7 Points**
8	'The Quiet American' was based on a book by which author?	**8 Points**
9	In what film did Arnie play a firefighter avenging the death of his family?	**9 Points**
10	What are Colleen's dying words in 'Signs'?	**10 Points**

62. Around the World

1	To which region of Romania is 'Van Helsing' sent to kill Dracula, in the 2004 film?	1 Point

2	Name the 2006 South Korean monster movie.	2 Points

3	In which South African city was 'Chappie' set?	3 Points

4	The music of which group is Muriel obsessed with in the Australian film 'Muriel's Wedding'?	4 Points

5	Who directed the 2000 Chinese film 'Crouching Tiger, Hidden Dragon'?	5 Points

6	In 'The Last Samurai', who plays the leader of the samurai?	6 Points

7	What German film was about a surveillance operator in East Berlin becoming obsessed with the people he watched?	7 Points

8	Name the French rape and revenge horror film from 2017.	8 Points

9	What is the famous Mexican movie about two teenage boys taking a road trip with an older woman?	9 Points

10	Name the French tragic romantic film from 2012 focusing on an elderly couple.	10 Points

63. James Bond

1	Who performed the theme song for 'Die Another Day', in which they also appeared?	**1 Point**

2	In 'Spectre', Christoph Waltz plays which villain?	**2 Points**

3	Who has produced all the Bond films starring Pierce Brosnan and Daniel Craig?	**3 Points**

4	Where is 'Casino Royale' in the 2006 film?	**4 Points**

5	What is 'Skyfall'?	**5 Points**

6	Which two people have played Moneypenny since 1995?	**6 Points**

7	Who appeared as Colonel Wai Lin in 'Tomorrow Never Dies'?	**7 Points**

8	At what sort of factory does Bond accost Zukovsky in 'The World Is Not Enough'?	**8 Points**

9	Where are James and Natalya escorted to at the end of 'GoldenEye'?	**9 Points**

10	At the start of 'Quantum of Solace', who does Bond have in the boot of his car?	**10 Points**

64. Dwayne Johnson Movies

1	He starred in which disaster film from 2015, named after the fault line which causes an earthquake?	1 Point

2	In what film did he star as the title character, a historical king of Egypt?	2 Points

3	Name the character he played in 'Baywatch'.	3 Points

4	Who starred alongside him and Jason Statham in 'Hobbs & Shaw', playing the villain Brixton?	4 Points

5	Which British comedian directed and appeared in 'Fighting with my Family'?	5 Points

6	In what city was 'Skyscraper' set?	6 Points

7	In 'Jumanji: Welcome to the Jungle', what is the name of the magic jewel?	7 Points

8	What gift does Robbie give Calvin at the end of 'Central Intelligence'?	8 Points

9	In 'Pain & Gain', Johnson, Mark Wahlberg and Anthony Mackie portrayed a real-life gang known as who?	9 Points

10	For what fictional American football team does his character play in 'The Game Plan'?	10 Points

65. Numbers

1	How old was Steve Carrell's virgin in the 2005 film?	**1 Point**

2	What number is the submarine in the 2000 film?	**2 Points**

3	With which number does Jim Carrey's character become obsessed in the 2007 film?	**3 Points**

4	According to the Seth McFarlane film, how many ways were there to die in the west?	**4 Points**

5	What number follows 'Super' in the 2011 sci-fi film set in the 1970s?	**5 Points**

6	How many blocks did Bruce Willis need to transport Mos Def in the 2006 film?	**6 Points**

7	What was the title of the film starring Jim Sturgess as a college student turned card counter?	**7 Points**

8	What hour was the film which starred Edward Norton as a man with one more day of freedom before going to prison?	**8 Points**

9	What British crime drama, centred around four 19 year-old girls, was written and co-directed by Noel Clarke?	**9 Points**

10	How many ghosts are in the title of a horror film from 2001, a remake of a 1960 film of the same name?	**10 Points**

66. 2003

1	Who or what is 'Seabiscuit'?	**1 Point**
2	In what film did Eddie Murphy open a day care business with a friend?	**2 Points**
3	Name the second and third installments in the 'Matrix' trilogy, both released in 2003.	**3 Points**
4	Which fantasy sequel won the Best Director and Best Picture Oscars?	**4 Points**
5	Who starred as a CIA trainee in 'The Recruit'?	**5 Points**
6	In what city was 'Mystic River' set?	**6 Points**
7	Who two actors starred as police detectives in 'Hollywood Homicide'?	**7 Points**
8	In '28 Days Later', what vehicle do Jim, Selena, Frank and Hannah travel to Manchester in?	**8 Points**
9	Who played John Connor in 'Terminator 3: Rise of the Machines'?	**9 Points**
10	Which 2003 movie became the first western film to air on North Korean state television when it was shown in 2010?	**10 Points**

67. Sigourney Weaver Movies

1	Reprising the role for the third time in 1992's Alien^3, what was Weaver's character called?	**1 Point**
2	In what 2016 remake did she make an appearance alongside other cast members from the original film?	**2 Points**
3	Who starred with her in 'Dave' as the President and fake President of the USA?	**3 Points**
4	What film saw her star alongside Tim Allen and Alan Rickman as TV stars taken into space?	**4 Points**
5	She played a surrogate agent in which comedy film from 2008 starring Tina Fey and Amy Poehler?	**5 Points**
6	What character does she play in 'Avatar'?	**6 Points**
7	What is her character's occupation in 'Red Lights'?	**7 Points**
8	In which 2006 drama did she appear as Babe Paley?	**8 Points**
9	In 'Heartbreakers', which song does she sing on stage whilst pretending to be Russian?	**9 Points**
10	Which character did she play in the 2011 film 'Paul', about a rude alien?	**10 Points**

68. Disney

1	Which 1995 film was based on the life of a Native American woman?	**1 Point**
2	'Mulan' was based on a legend from which country?	**2 Points**
3	On which fairy tale was 'Tangled' loosely based?	**3 Points**
4	In what film from 2011 do the residents of Hundred Acre Wood go on an adventure?	**4 Points**
5	David Spade voiced 'Emperor Kuzco' in which film?	**5 Points**
6	In what film does Cuba Gooding Jr inherit a team of sled dogs?	**6 Points**
7	What breed of dog is 'Bolt'?	**7 Points**
8	Who voiced 'Chicken Little' in the 2005 film?	**8 Points**
9	In 'The Hunchback of Notre Dame', what are the names of the gargoyles to whom Quasimodo talks?	**9 Points**
10	Who voiced Belle in the 1991 film 'Beauty and the Beast'?	**10 Points**

1 point for each film identified

1	2	3
PERKING OVERLY & AGER	YET YOU CLOG	VETTING SAGGIEST HOOM

4	5	6
FAZED TURK SHOD HAZE	HANK TIPPER THEN	SEEN A HAT CLAD VEST

7	8	9
CUP KONKED	U FLOW BE	PLEASE NIX PEPPERS

10
WET SHAVING PAN SHAPE

70. Sylvester Stallone Movies

1	In what action film from 1996 does he try to save survivors trapped in a tunnel?	**1 Point**
2	He appeared as Stakar Ogord in which superhero sequel of 2017?	**2 Points**
3	What is the name of his real-life son, who played his on-screen son In 'Rocky V'?	**3 Points**
4	Estelle Getty starred as his mother in what film?	**4 Points**
5	He stars as a mob enforcer in which film, a remake of a 1971 film of the same name?	**5 Points**
6	In 'Assassins', he is hired to kill a computer hacker, played by whom?	**6 Points**
7	In 2008's 'Rambo', John Rambo leads a team to rescue missionaries from which South East Asian country?	**7 Points**
8	In 'Escape Plan', what does his character make in order to work out where the prison is?	**8 Points**
9	In 'Cliffhanger', what is in the three lost briefcases?	**9 Points**
10	In 'Cop Land', what physical issue stopped Sly's character from becoming an NYPD cop?	**10 Points**

71. 2004

1	What was the second film to star George Clooney and Brad Pitt planning an elaborate heist?	**1 Point**
2	Adam Sandler and Drew Barrymore reunited for which romcom?	**2 Points**
3	Jim Caviezel starred as Jesus Christ in what film?	**3 Points**
4	Who appeared as Ben Stiller's best friend in 'Along Came Polly'?	**4 Points**
5	Jamie Foxx won an Oscar, BAFTA and Golden Globe for his portrayal of which real-life musician?	**5 Points**
6	In the film 'Dawn of the Dead', where did the survivors take refuge?	**6 Points**
7	Who becomes class president in 'Napoleon Dynamite'?	**7 Points**
8	The Coen Brothers directed Tom Hanks in what remake?	**8 Points**
9	Which TV and film star wrote the screenplay for 'Mean Girls'?	**9 Points**
10	What is Tom Cruise's hitman called in 'Collateral'?	**10 Points**

72. Netflix Originals

1	Who played the main character in 'Bird Box'?	1 Point
2	What was the name of the film released as a follow-up to the TV series 'Breaking Bad'?	2 Points
3	What 2018 drama set in Mexico City won the Best Picture Oscar?	3 Points
4	What 2017 film was about a girl who raises a genetically-modified superpig?	4 Points
5	What 2015 film was about a young boy in West Africa becoming a child soldier as his country goes through a horrific war?	5 Points
6	The third film of the 'Cloverfield' trilogy was entitled what?	6 Points
7	In which mountain range do Ben Affleck and Oscar Isaac get lost, in 'Triple Frontier'?	7 Points
8	What horror drama was based on a Stephen King novel and named after the year in which it's set?	8 Points
9	Name the 2018 British film about a terrible incident on a hunting trip.	9 Points
10	Who starred as Lara Jean in the 2018 film 'To All the Boys I've Loved Before'?	10 Points

73. Remakes

1	Which 1994 Disney film was remade in 2019?	**1 Point**

2	Lady Gaga and Bradley Cooper starred in which 2018 film, the latest of several remakes of the same story?	**2 Points**

3	In 'The Thomas Crown Affair' from 1999, a remake of the 1968 film, what does Crown steal?	**3 Points**

4	'Let Me In' was a remake of a film from which country?	**4 Points**

5	What film from 2015 was a remake of a 1991 Kathryn Bigelow directed movie of the same name?	**5 Points**

6	Where is the setting for the 1996 film 'The Birdcage', a remake of the 1978 French film 'La Cage aux Folles'?	**6 Points**

7	'The Hustle' starring Anne Hathaway and Rebel Wilson was a remake of which film?	**7 Points**

8	'The Departed' was a remake of which Hong Kong film?	**8 Points**

9	What psychological thriller, directed by Michael Haneke, was a remake of his own film made in Austria?	**9 Points**

10	'The Next Three Days', starring Russell Crowe and Elizabeth Banks, was a remake of which French film?	**10 Points**

74. Jim Carrey Movies

1	Complete the film title: 'Mr Popper's......'	1 Point
2	Who narrates the 'A Series of Unfortunate Events' in the film starring Carrey from 2004?	2 Points
3	In what film must his character always tell the truth?	3 Points
4	What is the name of the 'captain' he plays in 'Kick-Ass 2'?	4 Points
5	In 'Fun with Dick and Jane', who played Jane alongside Carrey as Dick?	5 Points
6	What is the name of the pet store that Harry and Lloyd want to open in 'Dumb and Dumber'?	6 Points
7	In what 2001 film does Carrey lose his memory and get mistaken for a long lost son?	7 Points
8	In 'Ace Ventura: Pet Detective', as well as the dolphin Snowflake, what animal is Ace trying to find for a sizeable reward?	8 Points
9	'I Love You Phillip Morris' saw him play which real-life person?	9 Points
10	In 'Eternal Sunshine of the Spotless Mind', what is the name of the firm that can erase your memories?	10 Points

75. Christmas Movies

1	Who stole Christmas in a 2000 film?	**1 Point**

2	Who created 'The Nightmare Before Christmas'?	**2 Points**

3	What 1994 Christmas movie starring Richard Attenborough was a remake of a film from 1947?	**3 Points**

4	What song does the character Jovie sing in the shower in 'Elf'?	**4 Points**

5	In 'The Muppet Christmas Carol', which character did Kermit play?	**5 Points**

6	Who starred as a couple visiting their families in Four Christmases?	**6 Points**

7	What is the name of the 2015 festive horror film starring Toni Colette and Adam Scott?	**7 Points**

8	Who voiced the title character in 'Arthur Christmas'?	**8 Points**

9	What is the name of the businessman that Patch the elf goes to work for in 'Santa Claus: The Movie'?	**9 Points**

10	What present does the Hero Boy receive from Santa in 'The Polar Express'?	**10 Points**

76. 2005

1	Which animated film was named after an island off mainland Africa?	1 Point
2	Peter Jackson remade which 1933 classic in 2005?	2 Points
3	Brad Pitt and Angelina Jolie met on the set of which film?	3 Points
4	Name the romcom starring Debra Messing and Dermot Mulroney.	4 Points
5	Which horror film sees a group of women head into the Appalachians?	5 Points
6	Frank Miller directed what film based on his own novel?	6 Points
7	In 'V for Vendetta', what is V's favourite film?	7 Points
8	In 'War of the Worlds', what does Tom Cruise's son call him?	8 Points
9	Who had the lead role in the film 'Transamerica'?	9 Points
10	Rachel Weisz won a Best Supporting Actress Oscar for her role in which film?	10 Points

77. Chris Evans Movies

1	Which Avenger does Evans play?	**1 Point**
2	Which of his characters uses the catchphrase "flame on!"	**2 Points**
3	Who co-starred with him in the 2007 police thriller 'Street Kings', playing Tom Ludlow?	**3 Points**
4	What is the name of the 2013 film directed by Bong Joon Ho set on a train?	**4 Points**
5	He appeared in which Danny Boyle film about a crew trying to reignite the sun?	**5 Points**
6	Name the 2009 film about people with telekentic powers.	**6 Points**
7	'The Red Sea Diving Resort' is set in which country in 1979?	**7 Points**
8	In 'The Iceman', his character befriends which real life serial killer played by Michael Shannon?	**8 Points**
9	In what 2010 film did he appear alongside Zoe Saldana, Jeffrey Dean Morgan and Idris Elba?	**9 Points**
10	In 'Cellular', what is the name of the kidnapped boy, who shares his name with a pop star?	**10 Points**

78. Real Life #2

1	Who starred as 'Malcom X'?	**1 Point**
2	What Steven Spielberg movie about the Holocaust won the Best Picture Oscar in 1993?	**2 Points**
3	Name the 2016 film about Katherine Goble Johnson, Dorothy Vaughan and Mary Jackson, who all worked as mathmeticians at NASA.	**3 Points**
4	Who starred as the title character in 'Dragon: The Bruce Lee Story'?	**4 Points**
5	Name the eccentic multimillionaire in 'Foxcatcher'.	**5 Points**
6	'Let Him Have It' from 1991 told the story of which man who was hanged?	**6 Points**
7	'La Vie En Rose' saw Marion Cotillard win an Oscar for portraying whom?	**7 Points**
8	Who starred as Tina and Ike Turner in the 1993 film 'What's Love Got to Do with It'?	**8 Points**
9	In 'The Aviator', what is the name of the huge seaplane that Howard Hughes builds?	**9 Points**
10	'Shadowlands' was about the relationship between which English author and American poet?	**10 Points**

79. Christopher Nolan's Batman Trilogy

1	Who won a posthumous Oscar for his performance in 'The Dark Knight'?	1 Point
2	Which actor played Bane in 'The Dark Knight Rises'?	2 Points
3	What is the name of Bruce Wayne's company?	3 Points
4	Which character publicly claims to be Batman in 'The Dark Knight'?	4 Points
5	Name the two stars who played Rachel in the trilogy.	5 Points
6	Who played Ra's Al Ghul in Batman Begins?	6 Points
7	Cillian Murphy played which villain?	7 Points
8	In the last of the three films, where is Alfred on holiday when he sees Bruce?	8 Points
9	What does Lucius Fox say to Earle at the end of 'Batman Begins'?	9 Points
10	Inmates from which prison are released by Bane in 'The Dark Knight Rises'?	10 Points

80. Drama #2

1	Matt Damon starred as a super smart janitor in which film?	1 Point
2	What 2008 Clint Eastwood film is named after the car belonging to the main character?	2 Points
3	Who received an Oscar nomination for her portrayal of school girl Jenny in 'An Education'?	3 Points
4	What 1995 film starring Whitney Houston is about four friends and their relationships with men?	4 Points
5	In 'Miss Sloane', what is the title character's political job?	5 Points
6	In 'Chocolat', at what time of year does Vianne open her chocolate shop, to the mayor's annoyance?	6 Points
7	Nick Nolte and Barbara Streisand starred in which 1991 drama, based on a Pat Conroy novel?	7 Points
8	Tim Robbins directed his wife as Sister Helen Prejean in which film?	8 Points
9	In 'Forever Young', what is the name of the project which puts Mel Gibson into suspended animation?	9 Points
10	In 'The Upside', how did Philip become paralysed?	10 Points

81. 2006

1	Who was in the water in the title of the M. Night Shyamalan film?	1 Point

2	Name the film based on a Dan Brown novel.	2 Points

3	'Happy Feet' is an animated film about what animals?	3 Points

4	What nanny did Emma Thompson play?	4 Points

5	Who picked up several awards, including an Oscar, for her role in 'Dreamgirls'?	5 Points

6	'Breaking Free' was sung by the lead actors and featured on the soundtrack of which Disney film?	6 Points

7	Which young star entered the beauty pageant in 'Little Miss Sunshine'?	7 Points

8	At what event did Gary and Brooke meet in 'The Break Up'?	8 Points

9	What psychological horror film was an adaptation of a 1999 video game?	9 Points

10	'Hollywoodland' told a fictionalised story about which actor's death?	10 Points

82. Sport #2

1	To whom does the title of the basketball movie 'Like Mike' refer?	**1 Point**
2	Will Ferrell and Jon Heder starred as ice skaters in which 2007 film?	**2 Points**
3	Who starred as Muhammed Ali in the 2001 biopic 'Ali'?	**3 Points**
4	What sport features in 'Talladega Nights: The Ballad of Ricky Bobby'?	**4 Points**
5	In 'Here Comes the Boom', what sport does teacher Scott Voss take up?	**5 Points**
6	Who starred as a failing golfer in 'Tin Cup'?	**6 Points**
7	Where does Ignacio work before he becomes a Mexican wrestler, in 'Nacho Libre'?	**7 Points**
8	What comedy from 2005 is about an American football game between prisoners and their guards?	**8 Points**
9	In 'Southpaw', who played the retired boxer whom Billy Hope befriends?	**9 Points**
10	Which real-life coach does Denzel Washington play in 'Remember the Titans'?	**10 Points**

83. Harry Potter

1	Who wrote the books upon which the films are based?	**1 Point**
2	Name the actors who play Harry, Hermione and Ron.	**2 Points**
3	Name the four houses at Hogwarts.	**3 Points**
4	In which year was the first movie released?	**4 Points**
5	The capture of which object ends a Quidditch match?	**5 Points**
6	What kind of monster lives in the Chamber of Secrets?	**6 Points**
7	What is the name of the spell Ron and Hermoine use to make their feathers fly in 'Harry Potter and the Philosopher's Stone'?	**7 Points**
8	In 'Harry Potter and the Chamber of Secrets', who says "Celebrity is as celebrity does, remember that"?	**8 Points**
9	Who played Aunt Petunia Dursley in the first film?	**9 Points**
10	In 'Harry Potter and the Goblet of Fire', who does Cho Chang go to the Yule Ball with?	**10 Points**

84. Julia Roberts Movies

1	In what 1990 film do medical students practice dying and resuscitation?	1 Point
2	What character did she play in 'Mirror Mirror', a movie based on Snow White?	2 Points
3	Who did she star alongisde in 'Conspiracy Theory'?	3 Points
4	What is her job in 1994's 'I Love Trouble'?	4 Points
5	In which ensemble romcom did she play an Army captain?	5 Points
6	She played a photographer in which drama from 2004, adapted from a Patrick Marber play?	6 Points
7	In what period drama of 1996 did she play the fiancée of the title character?	7 Points
8	What pet does she buy the children in 'Stepmom'?	8 Points
9	What is the nickname of her character in 'America's Sweethearts'?	9 Points
10	What three countries did her character travel to in 'Eat Pray Love'?	10 Points

85. Richard Curtis Movies

1	Which 1994 film launched Hugh Grant to stardom?	**1 Point**

2	Name the 2019 film directed by Danny Boyle, for which Curtis wrote the screenplay.	**2 Points**

3	What 1997 film did he co-write with Rowan Atkinson?	**3 Points**

4	Who played Hugh Grant's roommate in 'Notting Hill'?	**4 Points**

5	What song does the Prime Minister dance to in 'Love Actually'?	**5 Points**

6	'About Time' stars which two actors as the father and son who can time travel?	**6 Points**

7	In 'Bridget Jones: The Edge of Reason', what is the name of the morning TV show on which Bridget works?	**7 Points**

8	Name the horse in 'War Horse', the screenplay for which was co-written by Curtis.	**8 Points**

9	'The Boat that Rocked' told the story of which fictional pirate radio station?	**9 Points**

10	Curtis wrote the screenplay for what film set in Brazil, about teenagers who make a discovery in a rubbish dump?	**10 Points**

86. 2007

1	What movie was based on a long-running animated TV show?	**1 Point**
2	Who starred as Sam Witwicky in 'Transformers'?	**2 Points**
3	Ellen Page starred as which title character, a pregnant teenager?	**3 Points**
4	In the film of the same name, what is the '3:10 to Yuma'?	**4 Points**
5	In what film do John Travolta, Tim Allen, Martin Lawrence and William H Macy take a road tip on their motorbikes?	**5 Points**
6	Sean Bean starred in the title role in which horror remake?	**6 Points**
7	Who played the FBI agent who Mark Wahlberg teamed up with in 'Shooter'?	**7 Points**
8	The film '300' tells a fictionalised version of which battle in the Persian wars?	**8 Points**
9	In 'No Country for Old Men' what is the name of the hitman played by Javier Bardem, for which he received many awards?	**9 Points**
10	'Alpha Dog' was based on the real life kidnapping of whom?	**10 Points**

87. Comedies #2

1	Ben Stiller and Owen Wilson starred as male models in which 2001 film?	1 Point

2	Which brothers starred in the critically-panned 'White Chicks' from 2006?	2 Points

3	In 'The Inbetweeners Movie', where do the group go on holiday?	3 Points

4	At the end of 'Deadpool 2', we see Deadpool travel back in time to shoot Ryan Reynolds as he reviews the script for which film?	4 Points

5	In 'The Campaign', who plays the opponent of Will Ferrell's congressman?	5 Points

6	What British horror comedy was written by and starred Alice Lowe and Steve Oram?	6 Points

7	What causes the body swap in 'Freaky Friday'?	7 Points

8	From which fictional republic does 'The Dictator' come in the 2012 film?	8 Points

9	In 'George of the Jungle', what is the name of the gorilla who raised George?	9 Points

10	What intelligence agency is at the centre of 'Get Smart'?	10 Points

88. Best Picture Oscar Winners

1	Which sport featured in 'Million Dollar Baby'?	**1 Point**

2	In what city was 'Crash' set?	**2 Points**

3	Kevin Spacey played Lester in which movie?	**3 Points**

4	'A Beautiful Mind' was about whose life?	**4 Points**

5	What Clint Eastwood directed film won in 1992?	**5 Points**

6	Including Best Picture, how many Oscars did 'Titanic' win?	**6 Points**

7	Based on a novel by Michael Ondaatje, what war drama won the Oscar in 1996?	**7 Points**

8	During the 1990s, which film became only the third to win the Oscars for Best Picture, Best Actor and Best Actress?	**8 Points**

9	What three names does the main character go by in 'Moonlight'?	**9 Points**

10	Name the main character in '12 Years a Slave'.	**10 Points**

89. Quentin Tarantino Movies

1	Who played the stunt double in 'Once Upon a Time in Hollywood'?	**1 Point**
2	Who played 'Jackie Brown'?	**2 Points**
3	Which Dusty Springfield song features in 'Pulp Fiction'?	**3 Points**
4	What is the name of the character nicknamed The Bride in 'Kill Bill'?	**4 Points**
5	In 'Reservoir Dogs', what character did Tarantino play?	**5 Points**
6	Tarantino directed one part of the Grindhouse double bill - Deathproof. Who directed the other half and what was it called?	**6 Points**
7	In which state was 'The Hateful Eight' set?	**7 Points**
8	Which hand signal gave Archie away when he was pretending to be a Nazi in 'Inglorious Basterds'?	**8 Points**
9	Under whose grave is The Bride buried in 'Kill Bill 2'?	**9 Points**
10	What mining company is Django sold to in 'Django Unchained'?	**10 Points**

90. Boats

1	What was the full title of the sequel to 'Speed'?	**1 Point**
2	What disaster movie from 2006 was a remake of a 1972 film?	**2 Points**
3	What actor was the only person to appear in 'All is Lost'?	**3 Points**
4	In what film does Matt Damon kill Jude Law with a boat oar before dumping his body overboard?	**4 Points**
5	Who starred with Shailene Woodley in 'Adrift', a real-life story about a couple lost in the Pacific Ocean?	**5 Points**
6	During which conflict was 'Master and Commander: The Far Side of the World' set?	**6 Points**
7	What 2009 thriller starred Melissa George reliving the same events over and over again?	**7 Points**
8	In which film is Ashley Judd accused of killing her husband on their boat?	**8 Points**
9	What critically-panned film from 2002 was about two straight men mistakenly ending up on a "gays only" cruise?	**9 Points**
10	What is the name of the 'Ghost Ship' in the 2002 film?	**10 Points**

91. 2008

1	The first installment of which vampire film series starring Kristen Stewart and Robert Pattinson was released in 2008?	**1 Point**
2	'The Other Boleyn Girl' was a historical romantic drama about the love interests of which king?	**2 Points**
3	How many dressees were in the title of a romcom starring Katherine Heigl?	**3 Points**
4	What animated film featured the voice of Jack Black in the lead role?	**4 Points**
5	What was the name of the character played by Russell Brand in 'Forgetting Sarah Marshall'?	**5 Points**
6	In 'Sex and the City', what did Carrie wear on her head for the elaborate wedding?	**6 Points**
7	On which fictional Greek island was 'Mamma Mia' set?	**7 Points**
8	What movie starred Diane Keaton, Queen Latifah and Katie Holmes as workers at a Federal Reserve bank?	**8 Points**
9	Name any of the films in the fake trailers at the start of 'Tropic Thunder'.	**9 Points**
10	What is the name of the shape shifting ogre voiced by Nick Nolte in 'The Spiderwick Chronicles'?	**10 Points**

92. Period Dramas

1	Anne Hathaway starred as Jane Austen in which 2007 film?	**1 Point**
2	Who starred as 'Marie Antoinette' in 2006?	**2 Points**
3	Emily Blunt starred as a British queen in which film of 2009?	**3 Points**
4	Judi Dench received an Oscar for playing which person in 'Shakespeare in Love'?	**4 Points**
5	Name the protagonist in Vanity Fair.	**5 Points**
6	Who played King George III in 'The Madness of King George'?	**6 Points**
7	Frances O'Connor starred as Fanny Price in which 1999 adaptation?	**7 Points**
8	What character was played by Ewan McGregor in 'Miss Potter'?	**8 Points**
9	Who starred as Abdul alongside Judi Dench's Victoria in 2017 'Victoria & Abdul'?	**9 Points**
10	In 2013's 'Belle', which character raised Belle?	**10 Points**

93. Three Words #2

1 point for each film identified

1

mob
psychiatry
therapy

2

David
teddy
fairy

3

pill
author
shares

4

Lancelot
oxfords
pug

5

Medellin
border
tunnel

6

Reynolds
poison
breakfast

7

jeep
missing
truck

8

climbing
avalanche
K2

9

blind
Elektra
Bullseye

10

Castor
FBI
transplant

94. John Grisham

1	Who starred as the young lawyer in 1993's 'The Firm'?	**1 Point**
2	Name the other 1993 film based on a Grisham novel, starring Julia Roberts.	**2 Points**
3	Name the father and son who appeared together in 'A Time to Kill'.	**3 Points**
4	What 1994 film, starring Susan Sarandon and Tommy Lee Jones, is about a boy who has witnessed a suicide?	**4 Points**
5	Who starred alongside Danny DeVito in 1997's 'The Rainmaker'?	**5 Points**
6	What 1996 film was about a young man trying to win a reprieve for his racist grandfather who is on death row?	**6 Points**
7	In 'Runaway Jury' what sort of company is the defendant in the lawsuit?	**7 Points**
8	In which state is 'A Time to Kill' set?	**8 Points**
9	What 2004 Christmas comedy film was based on a Grisham novel?	**9 Points**
10	Which 1998 film starring Kenneth Branagh was based on a discarded Grisham manuscript?	**10 Points**

95. Musicals

1	Who starred as Eva Peron in 'Evita'?	1 Point
2	'Rocketman' from 2019 starred Taron Egerton as which British pop star?	2 Points
3	'Glitter' is a 2001 film starring which musical superstar?	3 Points
4	Fantine sells her hair and what else in 'Les Miserables'?	4 Points
5	What song from '8 Mile' won the Oscar for Best Original Song?	5 Points
6	Which future music star appeared in Sister Act 2: Back in the Habit?	6 Points
7	Name the band Jack Black is kicked out of at the beginning of 'School of Rock'?	7 Points
8	In 'Pitch Perfect', what song does Beca layer over 'The Sign' at the ICCA semi-finals?	8 Points
9	At which Rome film studios is Guido Contini working in 'Nine'?	9 Points
10	In 'The Phantom of the Opera', during which song is Carlotta given many gifts to make her stay?	10 Points

96. 2009

1	What fantasy film became the highest-grossing film ever at the time, with over $2bn in box office sales?	1 Point
2	Kathryn Bigelow won the Best Director Oscar for which film set during the Iraq war?	2 Points
3	Which sci-fi franchise reboot starred Chris Pine and Zachary Quinto?	3 Points
4	In what film do Jesse Eisenberg, Emma Stone, Woody Harrelson and Abigail Breslin make their way through the zombie apocalypse?	4 Points
5	Name the male and female leads of 'Duplicity'.	5 Points
6	What food do the aliens love in 'District 9'?	6 Points
7	What political thriller was a remake of a BBC series from 2003 of the same name?	7 Points
8	Who starred as the flamboyant Chinese gangster in 'The Hangover'?	8 Points
9	Who directed 'Moon', starring Sam Rockwell?	9 Points
10	Name the real-life person upon which 'The Informant!' was based.	10 Points

97. Box Office Flops

1	Johnny Depp played Tonto in which film from 2013?	**1 Point**

2	Name the 1995 swashbuckler starring Geena Davies.	**2 Points**

3	What battle in Texas was the setting for a film starring Dennis Quaid and Billy Bob Thornton?	**3 Points**

4	Guy Ritchie directed and co-wrote which film about a legendary king?	**4 Points**

5	Kevin Costner starred in and directed which post-apocalyptic film in the 1990s?	**5 Points**

6	What is the full name of the Dreamworks film about the pirate Sinbad?	**6 Points**

7	In 2002, Eddie Murphy starred in 'The Adventures of...' whom?	**7 Points**

8	What science fantasy adventure from 2018 featured Oprah Winfrey?	**8 Points**

9	Which 2018 film sees people forming mobile cities following a cataclysmic war?	**9 Points**

10	What film from 2001 is the most expensive video game-inspired movie ever made?	**10 Points**

98. Animals #2

1	Which comedian wrote, produced, and starred in 'Bee Movie'?	**1 Point**

2	What breed of dog is Scooby-Doo?	**2 Points**

3	What film from 2018 was about a prehistoric shark?	**3 Points**

4	In 'Homeward Bound: The Incredible Journey', what are the three animals trying to get home?	**4 Points**

5	Who starred as the cat in Dr Seuss' 'The Cat in the Hat' from 2003?	**5 Points**

6	What type of penguin is Cody Maverick, who dreams of being a surfer in 'Surf's Up'?	**6 Points**

7	Who wrote the book upon which 'White Fang' was based?	**7 Points**

8	In 'Garfield: The Movie', what is the name of Garfield's owner?	**8 Points**

9	What sort of bird is Blu, the main character in the animated film 'Rio'?	**9 Points**

10	What does the girl Yi name the yeti she finds on the roof of her building in 2019's 'Abominable'?	**10 Points**

99. Morgan Freeman Movies

1	He narrated the English language version of which French nature documentary in 2005?	1 Point
2	With whom did he star in 'The Bucket List'?	2 Points
3	In what 2014 Luc Besson thriller did he star as a scientist helping the main character?	3 Points
4	In 'Kiss the Girls', based on the James Patterson novel, what is his character's name?	4 Points
5	And he reprised his role from 'Kiss the Girls' in which follow up film?	5 Points
6	In what film does he make a prosthetic for an aquatic mammal?	6 Points
7	In 'The Power of One', his character trains PK in what sport?	7 Points
8	In 'Gone Baby Gone', where was the missing girl found?	8 Points
9	In 'High Crimes', in what capacity is he hired by Ashley Judd?	9 Points
10	How is his character, the CIA Director, killed In 'The Sum of All Fears'?	10 Points

100. Cameos - Name Who Appeared as These Characters

1	Slimy executive Les Grossman in 'Tropic Thunder'	**1 Point**
2	Walk-off judge in 'Zoolander'	**2 Points**
3	King John in 'Robin Hood: Prince of Thieves'	**3 Points**
4	A hotel lobby guest in 'Home Alone 2: Lost in New York'	**4 Points**
5	Jack Sparrow's father in 'Pirates of the Caribbean: At World's End'	**5 Points**
6	Nicholas' CSI girlfriend at the start of 'Hot Fuzz'	**6 Points**
7	Agent M in 'Men in Black II'	**7 Points**
8	Gas station attendant in 'Wayne's World 2'	**8 Points**
9	Ageing bank robber in 'Maverick'	**9 Points**
10	Harry's roommate Ice Pick in 'Dumb and Dumber To'	**10 Points**

101. 2010

1	Complete the title of the Dreamworks film: 'How to Train Your...'?	1 Point
2	'Exit Through the Gift Shop' was directed by which grafitti artist?	2 Points
3	Also the title of the film, for how many hours was James Franco's character trapped?	3 Points
4	Christian Bale lost considerable weight in order to play a boxing trainer in which film?	4 Points
5	In 'Kick-Ass', from what did Dave make his superhero outfit?	5 Points
6	Gemma Arterton and Martin Compston starred in 'The Disappearance of...' who?	6 Points
7	Who took a road trip with Zach Galifianakis in 'Due Date'?	7 Points
8	About what does the King give a speech at the end of 'The King's Speech'?	8 Points
9	Name the four actors who played 'The A-Team'.	9 Points
10	In 'The Social Network', Mark checks the math during one of the legal sessions - how much was the total he confirmed?	10 Points

102. Movies Based on Video Games

1	What film from 2016 is about some irate avians?	**1 Point**
2	Who starred as Alice in the 'Resident Evil' series?	**2 Points**
3	In 'Hitman', what do the hitmen have tattooed on the back of their heads?	**3 Points**
4	In what film do a group of Marines travel to Mars on a rescue mission?	**4 Points**
5	In which film are three martial artists summoned to a mysterious island to compete in a tournament?	**5 Points**
6	Which two film stars have played Lara Croft on the big screen?	**6 Points**
7	What animal mutates and wreaks havoc on the space station at the beginning of Rampage?	**7 Points**
8	What society does Callum Lynch try to defeat in 'Assassin's Creed'?	**8 Points**
9	Which planet do the Orcs invade in 'Warcraft'?	**9 Points**
10	In 'Street Fighter', who is Colonel Guile (played by Jean-Claude Van Damme) trying to bring down?	**10 Points**

103. British Movies

1	In which city is 'Twin Town' set?	**1 Point**
2	What crime film starring Daniel Craig was Matthew Vaughn's directorial debut?	**2 Points**
3	Who directed the 2016 film 'I, Daniel Blake'?	**3 Points**
4	Sam Riley and Samantha Morton starred as Ian and Deborah Curtis in which 2007 film?	**4 Points**
5	Julian Fellows wrote and produced which historical drama based on the successful TV series?	**5 Points**
6	Who starred as Richard in 'Dead Man's Shoes'?	**6 Points**
7	In what year was 'This is England' set?	**7 Points**
8	The British Muslim family featured in 'East is East' run what sort of shop?	**8 Points**
9	What painting is stolen in the Danny Boyle film 'Trance'?	**9 Points**
10	What punchline does Helen give to James' joke at the very end of 'Sliding Doors'?	**10 Points**

104. Brad Pitt Movies

1	Name the 2013 film about a zombie attack on the world.	**1 Point**
2	In what film did he appear as one of two brothers growing up in Montana, becoming a skilled fisherman?	**2 Points**
3	What character did he play in 2004's 'Troy'?	**3 Points**
4	What 1998 movie was loosely based on the 1934 film 'Death Takes a Holiday'?	**4 Points**
5	In the film of the same name, what is 'Fury'?	**5 Points**
6	How does his character Tristan die in 'Legends of the Fall'?	**6 Points**
7	In the animated film 'Megamind', which character did he play?	**7 Points**
8	In 'Ad Astra', his character goes searching for his father, who was last heard from after reaching where?	**8 Points**
9	In 'Spy Game', in what country is his character captured and imprisoned?	**9 Points**
10	Which actor played his younger self in 'Sleepers'?	**10 Points**

105. Europe

1	In 'Brooklyn', from which country does Eilis migrate to New York?	1 Point
2	Wes Anderson directed what film about a concierge framed for murder?	2 Points
3	Where was Forest Whittaker 'The Last King of'?	3 Points
4	Name the Woody Allen film starring Javier Bardem, Penelope Cruz and Scarlett Johansson.	4 Points
5	Which Norwegian action thriller, based on a Jo Nesbo novel, starred Askel Henni?	5 Points
6	In 'Before Sunrise', in which city do Ethan Hawke and Julie Delpy fall in love?	6 Points
7	Which Swedish film from 2014 was about a man who abandons his family during an avalanche?	7 Points
8	To which island does Walter first travel in 'The Secret Life of Walter Mitty'?	8 Points
9	In what 2018 horror were American soldiers dropped behind enemy lines in France, where they discovered secret Nazi experiments?	9 Points
10	In which railway station does Hugo live, in the 2011 film?	10 Points

106. 2011

1	What film remake was about a young man who moves to a small town where dancing is banned?	1 Point
2	Who played the ex-boxer Charlie in 'Real Steel'?	2 Points
3	Don Cheadle starred alongside Brendan Gleeson in which Irish film?	3 Points
4	Who starred as a cancer sufferer in the film '50/50', with Seth Rogen as his best friend?	4 Points
5	Which music superstar's songs appeared in 'Gnomeo & Juliet'?	5 Points
6	What pop star had a role in 'The Smurfs'?	6 Points
7	Which actors played the three 'Horrible Bosses'?	7 Points
8	Who adapted their own novel 'One Day' for the big screen?	8 Points
9	On which night of the year was 'Attack the Block' set?	9 Points
10	Christopher Plummer won a host of Best Supporting Actor awards playing a father who had recently passed away, in which film?	10 Points

107. Name the Movie From the Tagline #2

1	All for one and one for all	**1 Point**

2	Wonder. Power. Courage.	**2 Points**

3	Nice planet. We'll take it.	**3 Points**

4	On the air, unaware.	**4 Points**

5	Here they grow again	**5 Points**

6	Inside every one of us is a special talent waiting to come out. The trick is finding it.	**6 Points**

7	Escape, or die frying.	**7 Points**

8	Upscale neighborhood, Down-home heart.	**8 Points**

9	Cocktails first. Questions later.	**9 Points**

10	Family isn't a word. It's a sentence.	**10 Points**

108. Denzel Washington Movies

1	He starred in a remake of 'The Taking of...' what?	**1 Point**
2	What is 'Unstoppable' in the 2010 film?	**2 Points**
3	He starred alongside Keanu Reeves in an adaptation of which Shakespeare play?	**3 Points**
4	In 'Man on Fire' he is hired to protect a nine-year-old played by whom?	**4 Points**
5	Who starred as a love interest in both 'Training Day' and 'Out of Time'?	**5 Points**
6	Name the 2017 film in which he starred as the titular idealistic attorney.	**6 Points**
7	In 'John Q', what operation did his character want for his son?	**7 Points**
8	As which real-life person did he star in 'The Hurricane'?	**8 Points**
9	Who played his wife in 'Fences'?	**9 Points**
10	What song plays on the radio at the end of 'Déjà Vu'?	**10 Points**

109. Bond Actors

1	Roger Moore had a cameo in which 1997 film, based on the long-running TV series in which he had starred?	**1 Point**
2	What is the natural disaster in 'Dante's Peak', starring Pierce Brosnan?	**2 Points**
3	In what Sean Connery movie do famous literary characters group together?	**3 Points**
4	In 'Hot Fuzz', Timothy Dalton played Simon Skinner, who owned what store?	**4 Points**
5	In what psychological thriller did Rachel Weisz and Daniel Craig star as a married couple?	**5 Points**
6	In what film did Pierce Brosnan star as one of four people who meet on New Year's Eve, all contemplating suicide?	**6 Points**
7	What character does Timothy Dalton voice in 'Toy Story 3' and 'Toy Story 4'?	**7 Points**
8	When Sean Connery's character Mason escapes from the hotel in 'The Rock', what vehicle does he steal?	**8 Points**
9	In 'Defiance', Daniel Craig plays one of four brothers who escape the Nazis by hiding in which country's forest?	**9 Points**
10	In what building is the big heist that Sean Connery and Catherine Zeta Jones carry out in 'Entrapment'?	**10 Points**

110. Thrillers #2

1	What titular animal does Jack Nicholson become in the 1994 film?	1 Point
2	What film from 2009 starred Gerard Butler as a man seeking vengeance for the murder of his family?	2 Points
3	'A Perfect Murder' is a remake of which Hitchcock film from the 1950s?	3 Points
4	Sharon Stone and William Baldwin starred in which erotic thriller set in a New York high-rise?	4 Points
5	For what is Hugh Jackman hired in 'Swordfish'?	5 Points
6	In 'Inside Man', the robbers all take variants of what name as their aliases?	6 Points
7	Who appears as Keanu Reeves' wife in 'The Devil's Advocate'?	7 Points
8	In 'Traffic', how is the cocaine smuggled?	8 Points
9	Who starred in 'Deceived', about a woman who finds out her dead husband was leading a double life?	9 Points
10	In 'Primal Fear', from what psychiatric condition does Aaron Stampler suffer?	10 Points

111. 2012

1	Who won the Best Original Song Oscar for 'Skyfall', from the James Bond film of the same name?	1 Point
2	'Argo' centred around the hostage crisis of 1979-81 in which country?	2 Points
3	Which box office bomb was directed by Madonna?	3 Points
4	In 'Man on a Ledge', Sam Worthington had been accused of stealing what?	4 Points
5	In 'The Best Exotic Marigold Hotel', Judi Dench travelled to India to confront whom?	5 Points
6	What was the name of Michael Fassbender's android in 'Prometheus'?	6 Points
7	Who played the title role in one of the most expensive films ever made, 'John Carter'?	7 Points
8	Ralph Fiennes' directorial debut was which Shakespeare adaptation?	8 Points
9	In 'This Means War', what game does Tuck take Lauren to play on one of their dates?	9 Points
10	In 'Looper', what is the name of the person in the future who has mighty powers?	10 Points

112. Name the Movie From the Quote #2

1	"That'll do pig, that'll do."	**1 Point**
2	"Chewie, we're home."	**2 Points**
3	"I drink your milkshake."	**3 Points**
4	"Always be closing."	**4 Points**
5	"We can't have toys out on the market that may be dangerous."	**5 Points**
6	"The greatest trick the devil ever pulled was convincing the world he didn't exist."	**6 Points**
7	"As if."	**7 Points**
8	"I volunteer as tribute."	**8 Points**
9	"The law says that you cannot touch. But I think I see a lot of lawbreakers up in this house tonight."	**9 Points**
10	"Even artichokes have hearts."	**10 Points**

113. Mission: Impossible Movies

1	How many 'Mission: Impossible' films were released before 2020?	1 Point
2	Ethan Hunt climbs the outside of which building in 'Mission: Impossible - Ghost Protocol'?	2 Points
3	Who starred as Nyah Nordoff-Hall, who Ethan recruits, in 'Mission: Impossible 2'?	3 Points
4	From where do the team snatch Owen Davian in 'Mission: Impossible III'?	4 Points
5	To which opera does Benji win tickets in 'Mission: Impossible - Rogue Nation'?	5 Points
6	Who directed 'Mission: Impossible'?	6 Points
7	Name the virus and cure featured in 'Mission: Impossible 2'.	7 Points
8	What word is used to test the volume sensors before Ethan is lowered into a high-security room in the first film?	8 Points
9	Who plays IMF agent Hanaway who dies at the start of 'Mission:Impossible - Ghost Protocol'?	9 Points
10	Over what glacier are the bombs placed in 'Mission: Impossible - Fallout'?	10 Points

114. Sandra Bullock Movies

1	In what film does Bullock live her life online?	1 Point

2	Who did she star alongside in 'Two Weeks Notice'?	2 Points

3	In 'The Vanishing', who played Sandra Bullock's boyfriend, obsessed with finding her after she goes missing?	3 Points

4	In what 2006 romance did she reunite with her 'Speed' co-star, Keanu Reeves?	4 Points

5	For which film did she win the Worst Actress Razzie, the same year she won the Best Actress Oscar?	5 Points

6	In which future decade was the film 'Demolition Man' set?	6 Points

7	In 'Premonition', how does she see her husband die?	7 Points

8	In 'Miss Congeniality', which state does she represent in the Miss United States contest?	8 Points

9	In 'The Proposal', where does she work?	9 Points

10	In 'The Heat', what do the Mullins family repeatedly ask her, to see what job she does?	10 Points

115. Tom Hanks Movies

1	Who starred opposite Hanks in both 'Sleepless in Seattle' and 'You've Got Mail'?	1 Point
2	What is the volleyball called in 'Castaway'?	2 Points
3	In 'The Terminal', what does Viktor want to buy when he lands in New York?	3 Points
4	In which film did he play FBI agent Carl Hanratty?	4 Points
5	Who plays his romantic partner in 'Philadelphia'?	5 Points
6	Name the film about a team of female baseball players in which he played the coach.	6 Points
7	What 1996 music comedy film was Hanks' directorial debut?	7 Points
8	In which film does he travel to the Pacific island of Waponi Woo?	8 Points
9	In which French village does he find the titular character in 'Saving Private Ryan'?	9 Points
10	In 'Larry Crowne', what nickname do his classmates at college give him?	10 Points

116. 2013

1	Which Superman movie starred Henry Cavill in the lead role?	1 Point
2	In which film are celebrities stuck in James Franco's house during the apocalypse?	2 Points
3	Who played the 'Identity Thief' in the film?	3 Points
4	What nationality were the pirates in 'Captain Phillips'?	4 Points
5	Where does Owen get a summer job in 'The Way Way Back'?	5 Points
6	In 'The Great Gatsby', what sport does Jordan Baker play?	6 Points
7	Which film, featuring 14 different storylines, was panned by critics with some calling it the worst film ever made?	7 Points
8	What is the name of Joaquin Phoenix's artificially intelligent virtual assistant in 'Her'?	8 Points
9	'Delivery Man', starring Vince Vaughn, was a remake of which French film, also the alias his character used at the sperm bank?	9 Points
10	Park Chan-wook made his English language directorial debut with which drama?	10 Points

117. Romance

1	In 1999, Julia Roberts starred as a runaway what?	**1 Point**

2	Who starred as the maid in 'Maid in Manhattan'?	**2 Points**

3	'Last Christmas' features music from which artists?	**3 Points**

4	Which actors played the lead roles in 'One Fine Day'?	**4 Points**

5	What country do the main characters visit in 'Sex and the City 2'?	**5 Points**

6	Who goes to work for a circus as a vet in 'Water for Elephants'?	**6 Points**

7	What 1995 film, starring Keanu Reeves, was based on 1942's 'Four Steps in the Clouds'?	**7 Points**

8	In 'Bridget Jones' Baby', what is the name of Patrick Dempsey's character, who may or may not be the father of the baby?	**8 Points**

9	What concert does Andie take Ben to, instead of a New York Knicks game, in 'How to Lose a Guy in 10 Days'?	**9 Points**

10	In 'No Strings Attached', where did the two main characters originally meet?	**10 Points**

Name the 10 most recent Best Actress Oscar Winners (for films from 2010 to 2019)

119. Jennifer Lawrence Movies

1	Her breakthrough came playing a poverty stricken teenager in which 2010 film?	**1 Point**
2	Where is the house located, in the 2012 thriller also starring Elisabeth Shue?	**2 Points**
3	Who played her con-man husband in 'American Hustle'?	**3 Points**
4	Name the film, in which she had a small part, that sees Mel Gibson start talking through a hand puppet.	**4 Points**
5	In what film did she play a Russian spy?	**5 Points**
6	Who directed the psychological horror 'Mother!'?	**6 Points**
7	In 'Passengers', which actor appeared as the android barman that she confides in?	**7 Points**
8	What sort of business does she run with husband Bradley Cooper, in 'Serena'?	**8 Points**
9	In 'The Hunger Games: Mockingjay', what does President Snow leave in her room to signify that he will always know where she is?	**9 Points**
10	What Stevie Wonder song starts off the dance routine Tiffany and Pat perform at the end of 'Silver Linings Playbook'?	**10 Points**

120. Star Wars

1	In what year was 'Episode I - The Phantom Menace' released?	1 Point

2	Who voiced Darth Vader?	2 Points

3	Who was Kylo Ren's father?	3 Points

4	What is the name of the new droid introduced in 'The Rise of Skywalker'?	4 Points

5	As which character did Oscar Isaac star?	5 Points

6	In 'The Last Jedi', General Hux is aboard which craft while planning to attack the Resistance base?	6 Points

7	What is the name of Padme's decoy who is killed at the start of 'Attack of the Clones'?	7 Points

8	What is Finn's Stormtrooper designation?	8 Points

9	Where did George Lucas make a cameo in 'Revenge of the Sith'?	9 Points

10	Who is the only actor to have appeared in all Star Wars films, and what character did he play?	10 Points

121. 2014

1	What film was about the life of Professor Stephen Hawking?	1 Point
2	Brendan O'Carroll wrote and starred in which film, based on his sitcom?	2 Points
3	Where do Channing Tatum and Jonah Hill go undercover in '22 Jump Street'?	3 Points
4	Who starred as Tris Prior, in the first installment of the 'Divergent' series?	4 Points
5	'Pompeii' was based on the events following the eruption of Mt. Vesuvius in which year?	5 Points
6	What Biblical drama film starred Russell Crowe and Emma Watson?	6 Points
7	What song is played during Peter Quill's first scene as an adult in 'Guardians of the Galaxy'?	7 Points
8	In 'Million Dollar Arm', John Hamm's sports agent goes to India to look for new talent in what sport?	8 Points
9	'Godzilla' fights parasitic monsters known as what?	9 Points
10	Jason Bateman directed and starred in what film about an adult who enters a spelling bee contest?	10 Points

122. Animation #2

1	What does 'The BFG' stand for in the 2016 film?	**1 Point**

2	In the film, what sort of animal is 'Turbo'?	**2 Points**

3	In the 2009 3D film 'A Christmas Carol', who played Ebenezer Scrooge?	**3 Points**

4	Who is Charlie Brown's love interest in 'The Peanuts Movie' of 2006?	**4 Points**

5	In which film does Ewan McGregor voice an aspiring inventor?	**5 Points**

6	Which British comedian and actor voiced Silus Ramsbottom in 'Despicable Me 2'?	**6 Points**

7	In what town does 'Rango' accidentally end up, where he becomes the hero?	**7 Points**

8	In 'Cloudy with a Chance of Meatballs', to what is the island of Swallow Falls renamed?	**8 Points**

9	In 'Hercules', who are Hercules' parents?	**9 Points**

10	In 'Meet the Robinsons', what is the name of the man who Lewis and Wilbur try to track down?	**10 Points**

123. Samuel L Jackson Movies

1	Complete the name of the 2017 comedy: 'The Hitman's...'?	**1 Point**
2	In 'xXx' he played an NSA Agent who recruits Xander Cage, played by whom?	**2 Points**
3	He and John Cusack starred in the psychological horror '1408', but what is 1408?	**3 Points**
4	Name the 1996 action thriller in which he appeared alongside Geena Davis.	**4 Points**
5	Who starred as Shaft's uncle in the 2000 film?	**5 Points**
6	He appears as Pat Novak in which Detroit-set futuristic remake of 2014?	**6 Points**
7	Who starred with him in the war film 'Rules of Engagement'?	**7 Points**
8	Where were both main characters going when they collided in 'Changing Lanes'?	**8 Points**
9	What is his character's nickname in 2003's 'S.W.A.T.'?	**9 Points**
10	In 'Jumper', what is the name of the group of which his character is the leader?	**10 Points**

124. Name the Movie From the Featured Song #2

1	'Let It Go' by Idina Menzel	**1 Point**
2	'A Whole New World' by Brad Kane and Lea Salonga	**2 Points**
3	'Everything is Awesome' by Tegan and Sara with The Lonely Island	**3 Points**
4	'Lady Marmalade' by Christina Aguilera, Pink, Lil Kim, Mya and Missy Elliot	**4 Points**
5	'Gangsta's Paradise' by Coolio	**5 Points**
6	'Glory' by John Legend and Common	**6 Points**
7	'Can't Stop the Feeling' by Justin Timberlake	**7 Points**
8	'Kiss Me' by Sixpence None The Richer	**8 Points**
9	'Listen' by Beyonce	**9 Points**
10	'Clubbed to Death' by Rob D	**10 Points**

125. Horror #2

1	What 1992 sci-fi horror film includes a bit of garden machinery in the title?	**1 Point**
2	Jennifer Love Hewitt and Sarah Michelle Gellar starred in which film from 1997?	**2 Points**
3	'Freddy vs Jason' featured the horror icons from which two film franchises?	**3 Points**
4	What 1998 slasher is about a series of deaths modelled on popular myths?	**4 Points**
5	Who appeared in 'Gothika' as a fellow patient in the psychiatric hospital in which Halle Berry is incarcerated?	**5 Points**
6	What is the name of the doll in 'The Boy'?	**6 Points**
7	Name the 2016 comedy horror starring Alice Lowe as a vengeful pregnant woman.	**7 Points**
8	Which character was the first person to die in 'Scream'?	**8 Points**
9	What song do Lee and Evelyn dance to while listening on headphones in 'A Quiet Place'?	**9 Points**
10	Which famous screenwriter and producer wrote her first screenplay for 'The Woman in Black'?	**10 Points**

126. 2015

1	What film told the story of a woman and her son held captive in a single room?	**1 Point**
2	Who wrote and starred in the comedy 'Trainwreck'?	**2 Points**
3	'The 33' told the real-life story of miners stuck underground in which country?	**3 Points**
4	Kevin Hart helped Will Ferrell prepare for prison in which film?	**4 Points**
5	What did the main character invent in the film 'Joy'?	**5 Points**
6	In which city is the opening scene of 'Spectre'?	**6 Points**
7	What was Joel Edgerton's directorial debut, in which he also appeared, alongside Jason Batemen and Rebecca Hall?	**7 Points**
8	Who played Ice Cube in 'Straight Outta Compton'?	**8 Points**
9	In 'The Revenant', what was the name of Hugh Glass' son, who he saw being murdered?	**9 Points**
10	What is the name of the Philadelphia gym in which Donnie trains in 'Creed'?	**10 Points**

127. Judi Dench Movies

1	What role did she play in several James Bond films?	**1 Point**

2	In which Agatha Christie remake of 2017 did she play a Princess?	**2 Points**

3	In 'Notes on a Scandal', where did she work?	**3 Points**

4	What character did she play in 'J. Edgar'?	**4 Points**

5	In which movie did she and Dame Maggie Smith play two sisters in a Cornish village?	**5 Points**

6	What is the name of the theatre that her character opens in 'Mrs Henderson Presents'?	**6 Points**

7	In what film did she appear as the mother of the main character, a recently-widowed man who hires an American nanny?	**7 Points**

8	What character did she play in the 2019 musical film 'Cats'?	**8 Points**

9	Who played the young Joan to her older Joan, in 'Red Joan'?	**9 Points**

10	Which role did she play in 2011's 'Jane Eyre'?	**10 Points**

1	...is 'The Great Wall' in the 2016 film?	1 Point

2	...is Louie held as a prisoner of war in 'Unbroken'?	2 Points

3	...was 'Captain Corelli's Mandolin' set?	3 Points

4	...is 'New Jack City' in the 1991 film?	4 Points

5	...was the Baz Luhrmann directed film starring Nicole Kidman and Hugh Jackman?	5 Points

6	...do Claire Danes and Kate Beckinsale get arrested in 'Brokedown Palace'?	6 Points

7	...did the events of 'Black Hawk Down' take place?	7 Points

8	...are tourists tortured and killed in 'Hostel'?	8 Points

9	...is Jodie Foster flying from in 'Flight Plan'?	9 Points

10	...does Gérard Depardieu take his daughter on holiday in 'My Father the Hero'?	10 Points

129. Gangster Movies

1	What film starring Tom Hardy was about the Kray twins?	**1 Point**
2	What Netflix film told the story of an ageing hitman recalling his time with the mob?	**2 Points**
3	Johnny Depp played legendary bank robber John Dillinger in which film?	**3 Points**
4	Which animated film featured the voice of Robert De Niro as the leader of an underwater mob?	**4 Points**
5	In which city was 'Gomorrah' set?	**5 Points**
6	In 'Donnie Brasco', what does Donnie refuse to remove at a Japanese restaurant?	**6 Points**
7	In 'Goodfellas', which character does Tommy shoot in the foot?	**7 Points**
8	Which casino did Sam run in 'Casino'?	**8 Points**
9	In 'Eastern Promises', who played the midwife who got mixed up with the Russian mafia?	**9 Points**
10	In 'Road to Perdition', what does Michael Jr answer when asked whether is father was a good or bad man?	**10 Points**

130. Will Smith Movies

1	In which 2019 film does Smith play a genie?	**1 Point**

2	What agent name is he given in 'Men in Black'?	**2 Points**

3	In 'Independence Day', what does his character say to the alien he shoots down?	**3 Points**

4	Alongside which female star does he appear in the films 'Focus' and 'Suicide Squad'?	**4 Points**

5	In which 2013 film did he star with his son Jaden?	**5 Points**

6	In which 1993 film did he play the best friend of a woman who discovers Ted Danson might be her dad?	**6 Points**

7	In the film 'I, Robot', what is the name of the robot who he first distrusts but then befriends?	**7 Points**

8	In 'Hitch', when he takes Eva Mendes to Ellis Island, what is the nickname of her ancestor whose immigration record they look at?	**8 Points**

9	The film 'I Am Legend' was based on a 1954 book by which author?	**9 Points**

10	In the opening scene of the film 'Bad Boys', how much does Mike Lowry tell Marcus his car cost?	**10 Points**

131. 2016

1	Complete the name of the animated film: 'The Secret Life of...'?	**1 Point**
2	Which two actors starred as 'The Nice Guys'?	**2 Points**
3	Which comedy movie was based on a successful British television series, with all female stars?	**3 Points**
4	Emily Blunt and Rebecca Ferguson starred in which thriller?	**4 Points**
5	In what horror film did a group of robbers break into a blind man's house?	**5 Points**
6	Which two legendary actors wrongly announced 'La La Land' as Best Picture at the Oscars?	**6 Points**
7	Who directed 'Batman v Superman: Dawn of Justice'?	**7 Points**
8	What is the villain Ajax's real name in 'Deadpool'?	**8 Points**
9	In 'War Dogs', the big deal that they underbid on was to provide 100 million rounds of what?	**9 Points**
10	In 'Eddie the Eagle', which event does Eddie decide to compete in at the end of the film?	**10 Points**

132. Stephen King

1	Pennywise the clown appeared in which film franchise?	**1 Point**

2	Which 1999 film starring Tom Hanks was based on a Stephen King book originally released in 6 parts?	**2 Points**

3	Name the 2004 film starring Johny Depp as a mystery writer, based on the novella by King?	**3 Points**

4	Jason Clarke starred in a 2019 remake of which film?	**4 Points**

5	What does Carrie have dropped on her in the 2013 film?	**5 Points**

6	What is the name of the "procedure" which Annie performs on Paul as punishment for trying to escape in 'Misery'?	**6 Points**

7	Kathy Bates followed up her 'Misery' performance by starring in which 1995 film alongside Jennifer Jason Leigh?	**7 Points**

8	What 2017 film starts with a woman tied up in bed?	**8 Points**

9	Who directed the 2007 film 'The Mist'?	**9 Points**

10	'Hearts in Atlantis' was loosely based on which Stephen King novella?	**10 Points**

133. 18 Rated Films

1	Who is famous for her crossed-leg scene in 'Basic Instinct'?	1 Point
2	As whom did Jamie Dornan star in the 'Fifty Shades' films?	2 Points
3	In 'Se7en', which sin is the final crime?	3 Points
4	In 'Sin City', how does Kevin, the main antagonist, die?	4 Points
5	Which character kills Dracula in the 1992 film 'Bram Stoker's Dracula'?	5 Points
6	In what game does Eddy lose £500,000 at the start of 'Lock, Stock and Two Smoking Barrels'?	6 Points
7	At the start of 'The Wolf of Wall Street', Jodan Belfourt tells us he earned how much money in the year he turned 26?	7 Points
8	Name the present Nick and Amy buy for each other for one of their anniversaries in 'Gone Girl'?	8 Points
9	Whose disappearence do Lisbeth Salander and Mikael Blomkvist investigate in 'The Girl with the Dragon Tattoo'?	9 Points
10	In 'Bruno', why does Sacha Baron Cohen travel to the United States?	10 Points

1 point for each winner named

Name the 10 most recent Best Picture Oscar Winners (for films from 2010 to 2019)

135. Al Pacino Movies

1	Pacino starred in the third part of which trilogy in 1990?	**1 Point**
2	In 'Insomnia', to which US state does his character travel to investigate a murder?	**2 Points**
3	In which film from 2015 did he play the title character, an ageing rock star?	**3 Points**
4	What was his character's nickname in 'Dick Tracy'?	**4 Points**
5	In what film from 2004, based on a Shakespeare play of the same name, did he play Shylock?	**5 Points**
6	In what Worst Picture Razzie winner starring Adam Sandler did he appear as himself?	**6 Points**
7	In 'Heat', what do his character and crew attempt to steal from an armored car?	**7 Points**
8	Where is Carlito fatally shot in 'Carlito's Way'?	**8 Points**
9	What is the name of the casino his character opens in 'Ocean's Thirteen'?	**9 Points**
10	What car does his charater test drive in 'Scent of a Woman'?	**10 Points**

136. 2017

1	What Danny Boyle film was a follow-up to the 1996 original?	1 Point
2	Complete the movie title: 'Film Stars Don't Die in...'	2 Points
3	Guillermo del Toro won Best Director awards for which film?	3 Points
4	'Battle of the Sexes' told the story of the real-life tennis match between which two players?	4 Points
5	Which character is turned into a clock in 'Beauty and the Beast'?	5 Points
6	Who voiced Batman in 'The Lego Batman Movie'?	6 Points
7	Tom Cruise won a Razzie for playing a U.S. Army Sergeant in which action adventure film?	7 Points
8	In 'Get Out', Missy hypnotises Chris into a trance she calls what?	8 Points
9	What syndrome does Auggie have in 'Wonder'?	9 Points
10	What do the three billboards say in 'Three Billboards Outside Ebbing, Missouri'?	10 Points

137. Cryptic Clues #2

1 point for each film identified

1	2	3
Ludo	**100/100**	

4	5	6
a b c d (e) f g h I j k l (m)(n) (o) p q r s t u v w x y z	Ro se	**skeyey**

7	8	9
mienidips	**Devotion**	

10
P E T S

138. Avengers

1	What is the name of Thor's brother, played on screen by Tom Hiddleston?	**1 Point**
2	Who wrote and directed 'Avengers Assemble'?	**2 Points**
3	Who plays Iron Man's love interest?	**3 Points**
4	Anthony Mackie plays which superhero?	**4 Points**
5	What is the real name of the character who becomes Ant-Man?	**5 Points**
6	As what do the Avengers refer to Natasha's ability to calm the Hulk?	**6 Points**
7	In 'Captain America: The First Avenger', what is the name of the science division of Nazi Germany's military?	**7 Points**
8	Name the three actors who have played Hulk on screen in the 21st century.	**8 Points**
9	They don't mention it in the films except for the credits, but what is Wanda Maximoff's superhero name?	**9 Points**
10	What cartoon-inspired nickname did Tony Stark use for Thanos' henchman Ebony Maw?	**10 Points**

139. Nicolas Cage Movies

1	In what film, about the events of September 11, did Cage appear?	1 Point

2	He stars as a motorcyle rider who sells his soul to the devil in which film?	2 Points

3	In what film does he voice a caveman called Grug?	3 Points

4	Name the two movies he starred in which have Vegas in the title.	4 Points

5	Who appeared as his brother in 'Lord of War'?	5 Points

6	In '8MM', he stars as a private detective looking into what?	6 Points

7	How far into the future can his character Cris see in 'Next'?	7 Points

8	The remake of 'The Wicker Man' sees his character travel to an island off which US state?	8 Points

9	In 'Knowing', what do the final two digits of the message mean?	9 Points

10	'City of Angels' was a loose remake of which German film set in Berlin?	10 Points

140. Action #2

1	What year is the setting and name of the film directed by Roland Emmerich, about a prehistoric tribe?	1 Point
2	Who starred as Lancelot alongside Sean Connery's King Arthur in the 1995 film 'First Knight'?	2 Points
3	Zach Snyder directed which superhero film set in an alternate 1985?	3 Points
4	What does Eli have to deliver to a safe place in 'The Book of Eli'?	4 Points
5	What 2016 film starring Mark Wahlberg told the true story of an oil rig explosion in the Gulf of Mexico?	5 Points
6	What film from 2009 was based on a toy created by Hasbro?	6 Points
7	What is the name of the valet and partner of 'The Green Hornet'?	7 Points
8	Who appeared as John McClane's son in 'A Good Day to Die Hard', the fifth film in the series?	8 Points
9	What is the MacGuffin in the film 'Ronin'?	9 Points
10	With whom is Earth at war in 'Pacific Rim'?	10 Points

141. 2018

1	Which film, based on the life of Freddie Mercury and Queen, was released in this year?	1 Point
2	Which superhero film starring Chadwick Boseman took over $1bn at the box office?	2 Points
3	Who tries to solve the disappearance of Blake Lively in 'A Simple Favour'?	3 Points
4	Name the documentary about a singer who had died in 2012.	4 Points
5	Which film starred Jason Bateman and Rachel McAdams as a married couple?	5 Points
6	Anna Faris starred in a remake of which Goldie Hawn film?	6 Points
7	'Bad Times at the El Royale' was set at a motel straddling the border of which two US states?	7 Points
8	In 'Ocean's 8', where do the women intend to steal the Toussaint necklace?	8 Points
9	'American Animals' told the real life story of young mean attempting to steal a copy of which valuable book?	9 Points
10	What Wes Anderson film was set in a dystopian near-future Japan?	10 Points

142. Trilogies

1	The original 'X-Men' trilogy was based on comic books by Jack Kirby and who else?	1 Point
2	What type of sports team are 'The Mighty Ducks'?	2 Points
3	Who directed the Spider-Man trilogy of 2002 - 2007?	3 Points
4	Upon whose novels were 'The Bourne Identify', 'The Bourne Supremacy' and 'The Bourne Ultimatum' based?	4 Points
5	In what language was the original 'The Girl with the Dragon Tattoo'?	5 Points
6	Who played Boromir in the 'Lord of the Rings' trilogy?	6 Points
7	Who played Dr. Evil's son Scott in all three of the 'Austin Powers' movies?	7 Points
8	In the 'Blade' films, what is the other name of Wesley Snipe's eponymous character?	8 Points
9	Which pair directed 'The Matrix' trilogy?	9 Points
10	Which film trilogy from the early 1990s was loosely based on the political ideals of France?	10 Points

143. Name the Movie From the Quote #3

1	"I am old, Frodo. I am not the same hobbit as I once was. It is time for you to know what really happened"	**1 Point**
2	"What I do have are a very particular set of skills."	**2 Points**
3	"They called me Mr. Glass."	**3 Points**
4	"I only talk this much before I kill someone."	**4 Points**
5	"Rock stars have kidnapped my son."	**5 Points**
6	"I don't like sand. It's all coarse, and rough, and irritating. And it gets everywhere."	**6 Points**
7	"If you're a bird, I'm a bird."	**7 Points**
8	"Would that it were so simple."	**8 Points**
9	"I'm hungry... in fact... I could use a snack."	**9 Points**
10	"Not quite my tempo."	**10 Points**

144. Keira Knightley Movies

1	In which film, based on the Jane Austen novel of the same name, did she play Elizabeth Bennett?	**1 Point**
2	Name the two actors who played her love interests in 'Love Actually'.	**2 Points**
3	In 'The Imitation Game' she solved what puzzle in a newspaper which led to her being recruited to work at Bletchley Park?	**3 Points**
4	In which 2001 film did she star alongside Lawrence Fox and Thora Birch?	**4 Points**
5	She starred in 'Never Let Me Go', which was adapted from a novel by which author?	**5 Points**
6	In 'Atonement', which tube station do we find out her character died in?	**6 Points**
7	She played the wife of which real climber in 'Everest'?	**7 Points**
8	Who plays her husband in the 2010 film 'Last Night'?	**8 Points**
9	She played whistleblower Katharine Gun in which film?	**9 Points**
10	Why did she faint at the start of 'Pirates of the Caribbean: The Curse of the Black Pearl'?	**10 Points**

145. Anagrams 2010s

1 point for each film identified

1	2	3
WHO HOUSED TWINE	ME SALLY MOG	PAY KIM DROIDY WAIF

4	5	6
THE DAB RACE	JAUNTER MUST BUTE HEAD	MUST THEN MEME NON

7	8	9
THE DRAG	SHUTS LER	HE IS VITT

10
PINCER IN A SMEAR

146. 2019

1	Which superhero film became the highest-grossing film of all time?	1 Point
2	Jordan Peele followed up 'Get Out' with which horror film?	2 Points
3	Who directed 'Parasite', the first non-English language film to win the Best Picture Oscar?	3 Points
4	Will Smith starred in which film as a former hitman and his clone?	4 Points
5	What film was released as a sequel to 'The Shining'?	5 Points
6	In 'The Long Shot', how does Seth Rogen know Charlize Theron?	6 Points
7	What was the main character's real name in 'Joker'?	7 Points
8	What horror film starring Florence Pugh centred around a Swedish festival?	8 Points
9	Which real life people did Benedict Cumberbatch and Michael Shannon star as in 'The Current War'?	9 Points
10	Which British film, set in Cornwall, won the BAFTA for Outstanding Debut by a British Writer, Director or Producer?	10 Points

147. Comedies #3

1	In what film did Arnold Schwarzenegger's policeman go undercover at a pre-school?	**1 Point**
2	Rick Moranis starred in which comedy sequel in 1992?	**2 Points**
3	Tina Fey and Amy Poehler starred as the title characters in which 2015 comedy?	**3 Points**
4	Who starred as the 'Monster-in-Law'?	**4 Points**
5	In 'David Brent: Life on the Road', which English rapper and comedian played Brent's bandmate Dom?	**5 Points**
6	In 'Meet the Fockers', what does Jack's cat Jinx flush down the toilet of the RV?	**6 Points**
7	In 'Stranger than Fiction', who plays the writer whose voice Harold hears in his head?	**7 Points**
8	What is the name of Bill & Ted's band in 'Bill & Ted's Bogus Journey'?	**8 Points**
9	Name the villainous children's television host in 'Spy Kids'.	**9 Points**
10	In 'I Love You, Man', Peter and Sydney bond over their mutual adoration for which rock band?	**10 Points**

148. Animals #3

1	What sort of animal was Willy in 'Free Willy'?	**1 Point**

2	In 'Horton Hears a Who!', what animal is Horton?	**2 Points**

3	What film from 2007 was about three rodent brothers who start a singing career?	**3 Points**

4	Who voiced Peter in the 2018 animated comedy 'Peter Rabbit'?	**4 Points**

5	Stevie Wonder and Ariana Grande performed the theme song 'Faith' for which film?	**5 Points**

6	In the 2019 action film 'Crawl', what animals hunt the main characters in their home?	**6 Points**

7	Who voiced Kaa the snake in the 2016 film 'The Jungle Book'?	**7 Points**

8	In 'Zootopia', to what role is rabbit Judy Hopps appointed?	**8 Points**

9	In 'Cats & Dogs', which actor, who had previously starred in a TV sitcom, voiced Mr Tinkles the leader of the cats?	**9 Points**

10	What is the name of the dragon in 2006's 'Eragon'?	**10 Points**

149. Rotten - Name the Movie with 0% on Rotten Tomatoes

1	An Italian film, based on the classic children's tale about a wooden puppet.	**1 Point**
2	John Travolta and Kirstie Alley returned in this film, with the pets being able to speak instead of the kids.	**2 Points**
3	Sean Connery and Christopher Lambert starred in this sequel to a 1986 action fantasy film.	**3 Points**
4	A couple adopted a brat in this 1990 "comedy".	**4 Points**
5	Unnecessary horror remake from 2016 about a group of five friends going to party at a remote cabin in the woods.	**5 Points**
6	John Candy and Richard Lewis starred in this Western adventure comedy film.	**6 Points**
7	Supernatural horror from 2008, about people dying after hearing a recording of themselves being murdered.	**7 Points**
8	Van Damme starred in this 2002 film about a special government agent assigned to protect a scientist.	**8 Points**
9	An "erotic" thriller starring Heather Graham and Joseph Fiennes, adapted from a Nicci French novel.	**9 Points**
10	Thriller starring Dominic Cooper, based on the novel series by Duncan Falconer of the same name.	**10 Points**

150. Fresh - Name the Movie with 100% on Rotten Tomatoes

1	The first outing for Woody and Buzz Lightyear.	1 Point
2	This film from 1993 was the second to feature Wallace and Gromit.	2 Points
3	A 2017 3D release of a 1991 movie starring Arnold Schwarzenegger (which only scored 93%)	3 Points
4	The second film in which Ben Whishaw voiced the main character.	4 Points
5	Biographical documentary about Philip Petit and his high-wire walk between New York City's Twin Towers in the 1970s.	5 Points
6	2011 British crime comedy direted by Dexter Fletcher, about a man who has just been released from prison.	6 Points
7	A 2018 drama based on the novel 'My Abandonment', about a man living in the forest with his young daughter.	7 Points
8	A documentary following the national football team of American Samoa as they try to qualify for the World Cup.	8 Points
9	A 1997 Canadian drama, starring Ian Holm, about the aftermath of a school bus accident in a small town.	9 Points
10	A horror sequel, starring Mark Duplass, about a video artist who goes to meet a man claiming to be a serial killer.	10 Points

ANSWERS

1. 1990

1. Home Alone
2. Teenage Mutant Ninja Turtles
3. 'Unchained Melody' by The Righteous Brothers
4. Nuns
5. Pretty Woman
6. Two Socks
7. 1885
8. Dulles International Airport, Washington DC
9. Chevrolet
10. Canaima

2. Colours

1. White Men Can't Jump
2. Blue Streak
3. Red Dawn
4. Black Sheep
5. Deep Blue Sea
6. Dora and the Lost City of Gold
7. Men in Black
8. The Hunt for Red October (Tom Clancy)
9. Black Swan
10. Red Dragon

3. Meryl Streep Movies

1. Madison County
2. Jim Broadbent
3. The Laundromat
4. Little Red Riding Hood
5. Her ex-husband (played by Alec Baldwin)
6. Emmeline Pankhurst
7. Bone marrow
8. Sister Aloysius
9. St. Clair Bayfield
10. "The Gauntlet"

4. Real Life #1

1. Walk the Line
2. Steve Jobs
3. McDonald's
4. Aileen Wuornos
5. India
6. Chris Hemsworth and Daniel Bruhl
7. Awakenings
8. Oakland A's
9. James J. Braddock
10. The Prince and the Showgirl

5. Tom Cruise Movies

1. Valkyrie
2. Emily Blunt
3. Oblivion
4. Frogs
5. Senator
6. Agatha
7. Auto parts store
8. Arsenal
9. Claude Monet
10. Lestat de Lioncourt

6. 1991

1. The Addams Family
2. JFK
3. Dustin Hoffman
4. Cape Fear
5. Harvey Keitel
6. Don't Tell Mom the Babysitter's Dead
7. Drop Dead Fred
8. John Goodman
9. Doc Hollywood
10. Berlioz

7. Name the Razzie Worst Picture Winner

1. Striptease
2. Catwoman
3. Fantastic Four
4. The Twilight Saga: Breaking Dawn – Part 2
5. Swept Away
6. The Emoji Movie
7. Battlefield Earth
8. Gigli
9. Hudson Hawk
10. The Love Guru

8. Hugh Grant Movies

1. Blue
2. American Dreamz
3. Aardman Animations
4. The Gentlemen
5. Cloud Atlas
6. Drew Barrymore
7. The Man from U.N.C.L.E.
8. Extreme Measures
9. Frankenstein
10. Wyoming

9. Dawson's Creek Actors

1. Scream 2
2. The Greatest Showman
3. Phone Booth
4. Ocean's 11
5. Ryan Gosling
6. Varsity Blues
7. Randi
8. Lay the Favourite
9. Maria Altmann
10. Matthias Schoenaerts

10. Magic

1. Fantastic Beasts and Where to Find Them
2. Salem
3. Fantasia
4. David Mitchell and Robert Webb
5. The Four Horsemen
6. Nikola Tesla
7. Her wand
8. Nora Ephron
9. Vienna
10. Manon

11. 1992

1. Under Siege
2. Basic Instinct
3. St Bernard
4. Aurora
5. A Few Good Men
6. The Hand That Rocks the Cradle
7. Lisle
8. Ben Kingsley
9. Deloris Van Cartier
10. "I shot the clerk?"

12. James McAvoy Movies

1. University Challenge
2. Mr Tumnus
3. Assassin
4. Edinburgh
5. It: Chapter Two
6. X Men: First Class
7. Wimbledon
8. Berlin MI6 station chief
9. Welcome to the Punch
10. 24

13. Anagrams 1990s

1. Green Card
2. Boyz n the Hood
3. Father of the Bride
4. My Own Private Idaho
5. Stargate
6. Natural Born Killers
7. Boomerang
8. The Crying Game
9. The First Wives Club
10. The Island of Dr Moreau

14. Jurassic Park Movies

1. Steven Spielberg
2. San Diego
3. B.D. Wong
4. Alan Grant and Ellie Satler
5. Gallimimus
6. Orlando
7. Indoraptor
8. Blue, Charlie, Delta and Echo
9. Barbasol Shaving Cream
10. Kirby Paint and Tile

15. Leonardo DiCaprio Movies

1. Romeo & Juliet
2. Alex Garland
3. Amsterdam
4. What's Eating Gilbert Grape
5. Spinning top
6. Martin Scorsese
7. Djimon Hounsou
8. The Aviator, Blood Diamond, The Wolf of Wall Street, Once Upon a Time in Hollywood
9. King Louis XIV
10. Pastries

16. 1993

1. Mrs Doubtfire
2. $1m
3. Richard Kimble
4. I Got You Babe by Sonny and Cher
5. Robert Duvall
6. Baltimore
7. Frank Marshall
8. San Francisco
9. The Lincoln Memorial, Washington D.C.
10. "Teddy Bear"

17. Cameron Diaz Movies

1. Shrek
2. The Mask
3. Los Angeles
4. Natalie
5. Vanilla Sky & Knight and Day
6. A Life Less Ordinary
7. Jon Favreau
8. 'these damn Nepalese coins'
9. Nikolaj Coster-Waldau
10. She has dyslexia

18. Name 10 #1

1. 2019: Joaquin Phoenix
2. 2018: Rami Malek
3. 2017: Gary Oldman
4. 2016: Casey Affleck
5. 2015: Leonardo DiCaprio
6. 2014: Eddie Redmayne
7. 2013: Matthew McConaughey
8. 2012: Daniel Day-Lewis
9. 2011: Jean Dujardin
10. 2010: Colin Firth

19. Mark Wahlberg Movies

1. The Italian Job
2. Transformers
3. Boogie Nights
4. Boston
5. Michael Jackson
6. Hindu Kush
7. John Paul Getty III
8. Tami-Lynn
9. 'Thunderstruck' by ACDC
10. Vince Papale

20. Cryptic Clues #1

1. Up
2. 3 Men and a Little Lady
3. What Lies Beneath
4. Broken Arrow
5. The Big Short
6. Big Hero 6
7. Knives Out
8. Little Women
9. Crossroads
10. The Favourite

21. 1994

1. The Lion King
2. Arnold Schwarzenegger
3. The BC-52s
4. Brandon Lee
5. Natalie Portman
6. 50 miles per hour
7. Serial Mom
8. Michael Crichton
9. $2m
10. Twenty-One

22. Pixar

1. Ant
2. Brave
3. Monstropolis
4. Coco
5. Waste Allocation Load Lifter: Earth-Class
6. Parr
7. Arlo
8. Bing Bong
9. Gasteau's
10. A blue tang

23. Harrison Ford Movies

1. Indiana Jones and the Kingdom of the Crystal Skull
2. Sean Bean
3. Regarding Henry
4. The IRA
5. Plane crash
6. Diane Keaton
7. Firewall
8. Jackie Robinson
9. Colombia
10. Bonnie Bedelia

24. Romcoms

1. Alabama
2. 500
3. Josh Hartnett
4. Crazy, Stupid, Love
5. Elle Woods
6. The Taming of the Shrew
7. Warm Bodies
8. Train station
9. Downton Abbey
10. Picture Perfect

25. Animals #1

1. Aslan
2. Zoo
3. Labrador
4. Caesar
5. George Clooney
6. Fish
7. The Grey
8. Richard Parker
9. Mr Jingles
10. 8 Below

26. 1995

1. Casper
2. The Brady Bunch Movie
3. Nine Months
4. Shallow Grave
5. 1970
6. Leather jacket
7. Agoraphobia
8. Amy
9. Cedar Creek
10. Summer in the City by The Lovin' Spoonful

27. Name the Movie From the Tagline #1

1. Psycho
2. Dirty Grandpa
3. My Girl
4. Jumanji
5. Monsters Inc.
6. AVP: Alien vs. Predator
7. I am Legend
8. Edward Scissorhands
9. Big Fish
10. Another 48 Hours

28. Westerns

1. Young Guns II
2. Cowboys & Aliens
3. A cattle drive
4. Kevin Costner
5. Preacher
6. Bad Girls
7. Emma Cullen
8. Harmonville
9. Pilgrim
10. "That's funny"

29. Kate Winslet Movies

1. J.M.Barrie
2. Iris Murdoch
3. Flushed Away
4. The Reader
5. Revolutionary Road
6. Australia
7. Collateral Beauty
8. Utah
9. Josh Brolin
10. Center for Disease Control

30. Space

1. Neil Armstrong
2. Interstellar
3. Alien: Resurrection
4. Potatoes
5. Alfonso Cuaron
6. Calvin
7. Pandorum
8. Vega
9. Lewis and Clark
10. Abbott and Costello

31. 1996

1. 101
2. Matilda
3. "Show me the money"
4. Dragonheart
5. $2m
6. The Long Kiss Goodnight
7. He gets fed into a wood chipper
8. From Dusk till Dawn
9. Radio vet
10. A copy of Herodotus' Histories

32. Thrillers #1

1. Hollow Man
2. Angelina Jolie
3. Ray Liotta
4. Chicago
5. The Ides of March
6. Pacific Heights
7. Saudi Arabia
8. P.D.James
9. Falls off balcony
10. Fenway Park, home of the Boston Red Sox

33. Name the Movie From the Quote #1

1. Brokeback Mountain
2. Braveheart
3. Meet the Parents
4. Sleepy Hollow
5. True Lies
6. National Treasure
7. The Help
8. Medicine Man
9. The Devil Wears Prada
10. The Parole Officer

34. Arnie Movies

1. The Expendables
2. Jingle All The Way
3. Batman & Robin
4. End of Days
5. Becoming a zombie
6. Total Recall
7. James Caan
8. Jack Slater
9. Michael Rappaport
10. Carl

35. Where in the World..... #1

1. Tibet
2. America
3. Queensland, Australia
4. The Hudson River, New York
5. Mexico
6. Rwanda
7. Japan
8. Zamunda
9. Turkey
10. Bolivia

36. 1997

1. Austin Powers
2. Harrison Ford
3. Hot Stuff by Donna Summer
4. Kevin Kline and Tom Selleck
5. Jennifer Lopez and Ice Cube
6. Starship Troopers
7. Spawn
8. Post-it notes
9. As Good as It Gets
10. Lerner Airfield

37. Three Words #1

1. The Inbetweeners 2
2. Alan Partridge: Alpha Papa
3. Backdraft
4. Maleficent
5. Doctor Strange
6. Batman Returns
7. Passenger 57
8. Grumpy Old Men
9. The Cable Guy
10. Old School

38. Comedies #1

1. Jackie Chan
2. Golf
3. The Dude
4. Topper Harley
5. The Plastics
6. Jonah Hill and Michael Cera
7. Naked Gun 2 1/2: The Smell of Fear
8. 50 Cent
9. Globo Gym Purple Cobras
10. "There isn't enough for wings"

39. Animation #1

1. Hop
2. Bugs Bunny
3. The Lorax
4. Saber-tooth tiger
5. Seth Rogen
6. Hawaii
7. Wings Across the Globe
8. Open Season
9. San Ricardo
10. "The Flushed Pets"

40. Bruce Willis Movies

1. 12
2. The Day of the Jackal
3. RED
4. The Last Boy Scout
5. The Kid
6. Wes Anderson
7. Raccoon
8. The Bonfire of the Vanities
9. "The Kansas City Shuffle"
10. "I was out of bullets"

41. 1998

1 Spice World
2 Lethal Weapon
3 Armageddon and Deep Impact
4 Steven Soderbergh
5 U.S. Marshals
6 Autism
7 Madison Square Garden, New York City
8 Malaysia
9 Grow Old With You
10 Brill

42. News

1 Ron Burgundy
2 Steve Carrell
3 San Francisco
4 Money Monster
5 Fox News
6 The Boston Globe
7 Jeremy Thompson
8 Good Night, and Good Luck
9 Katharine Graham and Ben Bradlee
10 Wolf Blitzer

43. Sport #1

1 Cool Runnings
2 Cheerleading
3 The Blind Side
4 Baseball
5 The Miami Sharks
6 Hoop Dreams
7 I, Tonya
8 The Basketball Diaries
9 Draft Day
10 William Ernest Henley

44. Travel

1 Aaron Paul
2 Hollywood stunt driver
3 Red Eye
4 Ansel Elgort
5 Doc Hudson
6 The Guilt Trip
7 The Colorado Rockies
8 Air Marshal
9 The Green Place
10 Cheryl Strayed

45. Weather

1 Twister
2 Waterworld
3 Nicolas Cage
4 Hard Rain
5 New York Public Library
6 The Fog
7 Solar flare
8 Poseidon
9 Wind River
10 Andrea Gail

46. 1999

1 Inspector Gadget
2 Will Smith
3 The Sixth Sense
4 The Blair Witch Project
5 Office Space
6 The woman in the red dress
7 The Bone Collector
8 Jane Krakowski
9 FBI Headquarters, Washington DC
10 South Glen High School

47. Name the Movie From the Featured Song #1

1 La La Land
2 The Bodyguard
3 Mermaids
4 Despicable Me 2
5 Armageddon
6 Batman Forever
7 Slumdog Millionaire
8 Casino Royale
9 Cruel Intentions
10 Bad Boys

48. Nicole Kidman Movies

1 Far and Away
2 Stanley Kubrick
3 Sean Penn
4 The Hours
5 Jersey
6 The Stepford Wives
7 DreamWorks
8 Blue Ridge Mountains
9 Malice
10 Casey Affleck and Joaquin Phoenix

49. Lord of the Rings

1. J.R.R. Tolkien
2. New Zealand
3. Smeagol
4. Sean Astin
5. Elrond
6. Seven
7. Three strands of her hair
8. Howard Shore
9. Saruman, Gandalf, Radagst, Pallando, Alatar
10. The war of wrath

50. Drama #1

1. The Lincoln Lawyer
2. Alcatraz
3. George Clooney
4. Best Supporting Actor for Mark Rylance
5. Turns it upside down
6. A Perfect World
7. Martin Sixsmith
8. Homer's Iliad
9. Rubik's cube
10. Snakes and children's clothes

51. 2000

1. Romeo
2. "Are you not entertained?"
3. Vin Diesel
4. O Brother, Where Art Thou?
5. The Cell
6. Bitch by Meredith Brooks
7. Sandra Bullock
8. PG&E
9. Flight 180 to Paris
10. Hank Evans

52. Adam Sandler Movies

1. Jewellery store
2. Jack Nicholson
3. Kevin James
4. Hair stylist
5. Click
6. Hotel Transylvania
7. Mr Deeds Goes to Town
8. Fourth of July
9. Frankenstein
10. South Central Louisiana State University

53. These Movies All Have "American" in the Title

1. American Pie
2. The American
3. American History X
4. American Gangster
5. American Factory
6. The American President
7. American Ultra
8. American Made
9. American Pastoral
10. American Psycho

54. Horror #1

1. Tremors
2. Candyman
3. Australia
4. Seven
5. Paris Hilton
6. John Kramer
7. Jack O'Connell
8. Patrick Wilson and Vera Farmiga
9. BEATNGU
10. Merman

55. Friends Actors

1. Scream
2. 17
3. Charlie's Angels
4. 6 Days, 7 Nights
5. Dumplin'
6. Bad Neighbours
7. Run Fatboy Run
8. Vincent Cassel
9. 3000 miles to Graceland
10. Don West

56. 2001

1. The Fast and the Furious
2. The Mummy Returns
3. Memento
4. Baz Luhrmann
5. The Mexican
6. There You'll Be by Faith Hill
7. Iris
8. George Jung
9. Tim Roth
10. Jewel

57. Action #1

1 Ben Affleck
2 Their adoptive mother
3 Jeff Bridges
4 Snake Plissken
5 Bird on a Wire
6 Liberty Island, NYC
7 Sahara
8 Khan
9 Turned to stone by Medusa's head
10 USS Alabama

58. Book Adaptations

1 Trainspotting
2 Fight Club
3 Jules Verne
4 Rita Hayworth and the Shawshank Redemption
5 Forrest Gump
6 BlacKkKlansman
7 L.A. Confidential
8 Persepolis
9 Katherine Paterson
10 Charles Portis

59. Food

1 Tomatoes
2 Charlie and the Chocolate Factory
3 Sean Penn
4 His own brain
5 Children
6 Julie & Julia
7 Annual giant vegetable growing contest
8 Octopus
9 7
10 Blue soup, omelette and marmalade

60. Film Scores / Soundtrack - Name the Composer

1 John Williams
2 Michael Nyman
3 Phil Collins
4 Hans Zimmer
5 James Horner
6 Danny Elfman
7 Clint Eastwood
8 Badly Drawn Boy
9 Ennio Morricone
10 Johnny Greenwood

61. 2002

1 Mouse
2 Submarine
3 My Big Fat Greek Wedding
4 Kristen Stewart
5 Diane Lane
6 Chicago
7 Christopher Nolan
8 Graham Greene
9 Collateral Damage
10 "Swing away"

62. Around the World

1 Transylvania
2 The Host
3 Johannesburg
4 ABBA
5 Ang Lee
6 Ken Watanabe
7 The Lives of Others
8 Revenge
9 Y Tu Mamá También
10 Amour

63. James Bond

1 Madonna
2 Blofeld
3 Barbara Broccoli
4 Montenegro
5 Bond's childhood home
6 Samantha Bond and Naomie Harris
7 Michelle Yeoh
8 Caviar
9 Guantanamo Base
10 Mr White

64. Dwayne Johnson Movies

1 San Andreas
2 The Scorpion King
3 Mitch Buchannon
4 Idris Elba
5 Stephen Merchant
6 Hong Kong
7 The Jaguar's Eye
8 Calvin's high school varsity jacket
9 The Sun Gym gang
10 The Boston Rebels

65. Numbers

1 40
2 571
3 23
4 A million
5 8
6 16
7 21
8 25th
9 4.3.2.1.
10 13

66. 2003

1 Race horse
2 Daddy Day Care
3 The Matrix Reloaded and The Matrix Revolutions
4 The Lord of the Rings: The Return of the King
5 Colin Farrell
6 Boston, USA
7 Harrison Ford and Josh Hartnett
8 A black cab
9 Nick Stahl
10 Bend it like Beckham

67. Sigourney Weaver Movies

1 Ripley
2 Ghostbusters
3 Kevin Kline
4 Galaxy Quest
5 Baby Mama
6 Dr Grace Augustine
7 Debunks supernatural phenomena
8 Infamous
9 Back in the USSR
10 "The Big Guy"

68. Disney

1 Pocahontas
2 China
3 Rapunzel
4 Winne the Pooh
5 The Emperor's New Groove
6 Snow Dogs
7 A white german shepherd
8 Zach Braff
9 Victor, Hugo and Laverne
10 Paige O'Hara

69. Anagrams 2000s

1 Kevin & Perry Go Large
2 Coyote Ugly
3 Something's Gotta Give
4 The Dukes of Hazzard
5 The Pink Panther
6 Save the Last Dance
7 Knocked Up
8 Beowulf
9 Pineapple Express
10 What Happens in Vegas

70. Sylvester Stallone Movies

1 Daylight
2 Guardians of the Galaxy Vol. 2
3 Sage Stallone
4 Stop! Or My Mom Will Shoot
5 Get Carter
6 Julianne Moore
7 Burma / Myanmar
8 A sextant
9 $100m
10 Deaf in one ear

71. 2004

1 Ocean's Twelve
2 50 First Dates
3 The Passion of the Christ
4 Philip Seymour Hoffman
5 Ray Charles
6 Shopping mall
7 Pedro
8 The Ladykillers
9 Tina Fey
10 Vincent

72. Netflix Originals

1 Sandra Bullock
2 El Camino
3 Roma
4 Okja
5 Beasts of No Nation
6 The Cloverfield Paradox
7 The Andes
8 1922
9 Calibre
10 Lana Condor

73. Remakes

1. The Lion King
2. A Star is Born
3. A painting
4. Sweden
5. Point Break
6. South Beach, Miami
7. Dirty Rotten Scoundrels
8. Infernal Affairs
9. Funny Games
10. Pour Elle

74. Jim Carrey Movies

1. Penguins
2. Lemony Snicket
3. Liar Liar
4. Colonel Stars and Stripes
5. Tea Leoni
6. I Got Worms
7. The Majestic
8. Dove
9. Steven Jay Russell
10. Lacuna, Inc

75. Christmas Movies

1. The Grinch
2. Tim Burton
3. Miracle on 34th Street
4. Baby it's Cold Outside
5. Bob Cratchit
6. Vince Vaughn and Reese Witherspoon
7. Krampus
8. James McAvoy
9. B.Z.
10. Silver bell

76. 2005

1. Madagascar
2. King Kong
3. Mr and Mrs Smith
4. The Wedding Date
5. The Descent
6. Sin City
7. The Count of Monte Cristo
8. Ray
9. Felicity Huffman
10. The Constant Gardener

77. Chris Evans Movies

1. Captain America
2. Johnny Storm / 'The Human Torch'
3. Keanu Reeves
4. Snowpiercer
5. Sunshine
6. Push
7. Sudan
8. Richard Kuklinski
9. The Losers
10. Ricky Martin

78. Real Life #2

1. Denzel Washington
2. Schindler's List
3. Hidden Figures
4. Jason Scott Lee
5. John Du Pont
6. Derek Bentley
7. Edith Piaf
8. Angela Bassett and Laurence Fishburne
9. H-4 Hercules / Spruce Goose
10. C.S. Lewis and Joy Davidman

79. Christopher Nolan's Batman Trilogy

1. Heath Ledger
2. Tom Hardy
3. Wayne Enterprises
4. Harvey Dent / Two Face
5. Katie Holmes and Maggie Gyllenhaal
6. Liam Neeson
7. Jonathan Crane / The Scarecrow
8. Florence
9. "Didn't you get the memo?"
10. Blackgate Penitentiary

80. Drama #2

1. Good Will Hunting
2. Gran Torino
3. Carey Mulligan
4. Waiting to Exhale
5. Lobbyist
6. Lent
7. The Prince of Tides
8. Dead Man Walking
9. Project B
10. Paragliding accident

81. 2006

1. Lady
2. The Da Vinci Code
3. Penguins
4. Nanny McPhee
5. Jennifer Hudson
6. High School Musical
7. Abigal Breslin
8. Chicago Cubs baseball game
9. Silent Hill
10. George Reeves

82. Sport #2

1. Michael Jordan
2. Blades of Glory
3. Will Smith
4. NASCAR
5. Mixed Martial Arts
6. Kevin Costner
7. A monastery
8. The Longest Yard
9. Forest Whitaker
10. Herman Boone

83. Harry Potter

1. J K Rowling
2. Daniel Radcliffe, Emma Watson, Rupert Grint
3. Hufflepuff, Ravenclaw, Griffindor, Slytherin
4. 2001
5. The Golden Snitch
6. Basilisk
7. Wingardium Leviosa
8. Gilderoy Lockhart
9. Fiona Shaw
10. Cedric Diggeroy

84. Julia Roberts Movies

1. Flatliners
2. Queen Clementianna (The Evil Stepmother)
3. Mel Gibson
4. Newspaper reporter
5. Valentine's Day
6. Closer
7. Michael Collins
8. Golden retriever puppy
9. Kiki
10. Italy, India, Indonesia

85. Richard Curtis Movies

1. Four Weddings and a Funeral
2. Yesterday
3. Bean
4. Rhys Ifans
5. Jump (For My Love) by The Pointer Sisters
6. Domnhall Gleeson and Bill Nighy
7. Sit Up Britain
8. Joey
9. Radio Rock
10. Trash

86. 2007

1. The Simpsons Movie
2. Shia LaBeouf
3. Juno
4. A train
5. Wild Hogs
6. The Hitcher
7. Michael Peña
8. Battle of Thermopylae
9. Anton Chigurh
10. Nicholas Markowitz

87. Comedies #2

1. Zoolander
2. Marlon and Shawn Wayans
3. Malia, Greece
4. Green Lantern
5. Zack Galifianakis
6. Sightseers
7. A chinese fortune cookie
8. Wadiya
9. Ape
10. CONTROL

88. Best Picture Oscar Winners

1. Boxing
2. Los Angeles
3. American Beauty
4. John Nash
5. Unforgiven
6. 11
7. The English Patient
8. The Silence of the Lambs
9. Little, Chiron, Black
10. Solomon Northup

89. Quentin Tarantino Movies

1 Brad Pitt
2 Pam Grier
3 Son of a Preacher Man
4 Beatrix Kiddo
5 Mr Brown
6 Planet Terror, Robert Rodriguez
7 Wyoming
8 For 3
9 Paula Schultz
10 LeQuint Dickey Mining Company

90. Boats

1 Speed 2: Cruise Control
2 Poseidon
3 Robert Redford
4 The Talented Mr. Ripley
5 Sam Claflin
6 The Napoleonic Wars
7 Triangle
8 Double Jeapordy
9 Boat Trip
10 SS Antonia Graza

91. 2008

1 Twilight
2 Henry VIII
3 27
4 Kung Fu Panda
5 Aldous Snow
6 Bird
7 Kalokairi
8 Mad Money
9 Scorcher VI Global Meltodwn / Satan's Alley / The Fatties Fart 2
10 Mulgarath

92. Period Dramas

1 Becoming Jane
2 Kirsten Dunst
3 The Young Victoria
4 Queen Elizabeth I
5 Becky Sharpe
6 Nigel Hawthorne
7 Mansfield Park
8 Norman Warne
9 Ali Fazal
10 Earl of Mansfield

93. Three Words #2

1 Analyze This
2 A.I. Artificial Intelligence
3 Limitless
4 Kingsman: The Secret Service
5 Sicario
6 Phantom Thread
7 Breakdown
8 Vertical Limit
9 Daredevil
10 Face/Off

94. John Grisham

1 Tom Cruise
2 The Pelican Brief
3 Donald and Kiefer Sutherland
4 The Client
5 Matt Damon
6 The Chamber
7 A gun manufacturer
8 Mississippi
9 Christmas with the Kranks
10 The Gingerbread Man

95. Musicals

1 Madonna
2 Elton John
3 Mariah Carey
4 Her teeth
5 Lose Yourself
6 Lauryn Hill
7 No Vacancy
8 Bulletproof
9 Cinecitta movie studios
10 Prima Donna

96. 2009

1 Avatar
2 The Hurt Locker
3 Star Trek
4 Zombieland
5 Clive Owen and Julia Roberts
6 Cat food
7 State of Play
8 Ken Jeong
9 Duncan Jones
10 Mark Whitacre

97. Box Office Flops

1 The Lone Ranger
2 Cutthroat Island
3 The Alamo
4 King Arthur: Legend of the Sword
5 The Postman
6 Sinbad: Legend of the Seven Seas
7 Pluto Nash
8 A Wrinkle in Time
9 Mortal Engines
10 Final Fantasy: The Spirits Within

98. Animals #2

1 Jerry Seinfeld
2 Great Dane
3 The Meg
4 Two dogs (a bulldog and a retriever) and a cat (himalayan)
5 Mike Myers
6 Rockhopper
7 Jack London
8 Jon Arbuckle
9 Spix's macaw
10 Everest

99. Morgan Freeman Movies

1 The March of the Penguins
2 Jack Nicholson
3 Lucy
4 Alex Cross
5 Along Came a Spider
6 Dolphin Tale
7 Boxing
8 At the police captain's house
9 Military Attorney
10 Stadium bombing

100. Cameos - Name Who Appeared as These Characters

1 Tom Cruise
2 David Bowie
3 Sean Connery
4 Donald Trump
5 Keith Richards
6 Cate Blanchett
7 Michael Jackson
8 Charlton Heston
9 Danny Glover
10 Bill Murray

101. 2010

1 Dragon
2 Banksy
3 127 Hours
4 The Fighter
5 A wetsuit
6 Alice Creed
7 Robert Downey Jr.
8 Britain's declaration of war on Nazi Germany
9 Liam Neeson, Bradley Cooper, Sharlto Copley, Quinton Jackson
10 $19,000

102. Movies Based on Video Games

1 The Angry Birds Movie
2 Milla Jovovich
3 Barcode
4 Doom
5 Mortal Kombat
6 Angelina Jolie and Alicia Vikander
7 A lab rat
8 The Templars
9 Azeroth
10 General M. Bison

103. British Movies

1 Swansea
2 Layer Cake
3 Ken Loach
4 Control
5 Downton Abbey
6 Paddy Considine
7 1983
8 A fish and chip shop
9 Goya's Witches in the Air
10 "Nobody expects the Spanish inquisition"

104. Brad Pitt Movies

1 World War Z
2 A River Runs Through It
3 Achilles
4 Meet Joe Black
5 A tank
6 Killed by a bear
7 Metro Man
8 Neptune
9 China
10 Brad Renfro

105. Europe

1. Ireland
2. The Grand Budapest Hotel
3. Scotland
4. Vicky Cristina Barcelona
5. Headhunters
6. Vienna
7. Force Majeure
8. Greenland
9. Overlord
10. Gare Montparnasse in Paris

106. 2011

1. Footloose
2. Hugh Jackman
3. The Guard
4. Joseph Gordon-Levitt
5. Elton John
6. Katy Perry
7. Colin Farrell, Jennifer Aniston, Kevin Spacey
8. David Nicholls
9. Guy Fawkes Night (5th November)
10. Beginners

107. Name the Movie From the Tagline #2

1. The Three Musketeers
2. Wonder Woman
3. Mars Attacks!
4. The Truman Show
5. Gremlins 2: The New Batch
6. Billy Elliot
7. Chicken Run
8. The Bervely Hillbillies
9. Swingers
10. The Royal Tenenbaums

108. Denzel Washington Movies

1. Pelham 123
2. A freight train
3. Much Ado About Nothing
4. Dakota Fanning
5. Eva Mendes
6. Roman J Israel Esq.
7. Heart transplant
8. Rubin Carter
9. Viola Davis
10. Don't Worry Baby by The Beach Boys

109. Bond Actors

1. The Saint
2. Volcanic eruption
3. The League of Extraordinary Gentlemen
4. The supermarket
5. Dream House
6. A Long Way Down
7. Mr Pricklepants
8. A Humvee
9. Belarus
10. Petronas Towers, Kuala Lumpur

110. Thrillers #2

1. Wolf
2. Law Abiding Citizen
3. Dial M for Murder
4. Sliver
5. Computer hacking
6. Steve
7. Charlize Theron
8. As dolls
9. Goldie Hawn
10. None - he faked multiple personality disorder

111. 2012

1. Adele
2. Iran
3. W.E.
4. Diamond
5. Call-centre staff
6. David
7. Taylor Kitsch
8. Coriolanus
9. Paintball
10. The Rainmaker

112. Name the Movie From the Quote #2

1. Babe
2. Star Wars Episode VII: The Force Awakens
3. There Will Be Blood
4. Glengarry Glen Ross
5. Small Soldiers
6. The Usual Suspects
7. Clueless
8. The Hunger Games
9. Magic Mike
10. Amélie

113. Mission: Impossible Movies

1. 6
2. Burj Khalifa
3. Thandie Newton
4. The Vatican
5. Turandot
6. Brian De Palma
7. Chimera and Bellerophon
8. "Toast"
9. Josh Holloway
10. The Siachen Glacier

114. Sandra Bullock Movies

1. The Net
2. Hugh Grant
3. Kiefer Sutherland
4. The Lake House
5. All About Steve
6. 2030s
7. Car crash
8. New Jersey
9. A book publisher
10. "Are you a narc"

115. Tom Hanks Movies

1. Meg Ryan
2. Wilson
3. "The Nike shoes"
4. Catch Me If You Can
5. Antonio Banderas
6. A League of Their Own
7. That Thing You Do
8. Joe Versus the Volcano
9. Ramelle
10. "Lance Corona"

116. 2013

1. Man of Steel
2. This is the End
3. Melissa McCarthy
4. Somali
5. A water park
6. Golf
7. Movie 43
8. Samantha
9. Starbuck
10. Stoker

117. Romance

1. Bride
2. Jennifer Lopez
3. George Michael and Wham!
4. George Clooney and Michelle Pfeiffer
5. United Arab Emirates
6. Robert Pattinson
7. A Walk in the Clouds
8. Jack Qwant
9. Celine Dion
10. Summer camp

118. Name 10 #2

1. 2019: Renee Zellweger
2. 2018: Olivia Colman
3. 2017: Frances McDormand
4. 2016: Emma Stone
5. 2015: Brie Larson
6. 2014: Julianne Moore
7. 2013: Cate Blanchett
8. 2012: Jennifer Lawrence
9. 2011: Meryl Streep
10. 2010: Natalie Portman

119. Jennifer Lawrence Movies

1. Winter's Bone
2. At the end of the street
3. Christian Bale
4. The Beaver
5. Red Sparrow
6. Darren Aranofsky
7. Michael Sheen
8. Timber
9. A white rose
10. Don't You Worry 'Bout a Thing

120. Star Wars

1. 1999
2. James Earl Jones
3. Han Solo
4. D-O
5. Poe Dameron
6. Star Destroyer
7. Corde
8. FN-2187
9. The Galactic Opera House
10. Anthony Daniels as C-3PO

121. 2014

1 The Theory of Everything
2 Mrs Brown's Boys D'Movie
3 A college
4 Shailene Woodley
5 A.D. 79
6 Noah
7 Come and Get Your Love by Redbone
8 Baseball
9 MUTOs (Massive Unidentified Terrestrial Organism)
10 Bad Words

122. Animation #2

1 The Big Friendly Giant
2 Snail
3 Jim Carrey
4 Little Red-Haired Girl
5 Robots
6 Steve Coogan
7 Dirt
8 Chewandswallow
9 King Zeus and Queen Hera
10 Bowler Hat Guy

123. Samuel L Jackson Movies

1 Bodyguard
2 Vin Diesel
3 A hotel room
4 The Long Kiss Goodnight
5 Richard Roundtree
6 Robocop
7 Tommy Lee Jones
8 Court
9 Hondo
10 Paladins

124. Name the Movie From the Featured Song #2

1 Frozen
2 Aladdin
3 The Lego Movie
4 Moulin Rouge
5 Dangerous Minds
6 Selma
7 Trolls
8 She's All That
9 Dreamgirls
10 The Matrix

125. Horror #2

1 The Lawnmower Man
2 I Know What You Did Last Summer
3 A Nightmare on Elm Street & Friday the 13th
4 Urban Legend
5 Penelope Cruz
6 Brahms
7 Prevenge
8 Steve, Casey's boyfriend
9 Harvest Moon by Neil Young
10 Jane Goldman

126. 2015

1 Room
2 Amy Schumer
3 Chile
4 Get Hard
5 A mop
6 Mexico City
7 The Gift
8 His son - O'Shea Jackson Jr
9 Hawk
10 Front Street Gym

127. Judi Dench Movies

1 M
2 Murder on the Orient Express
3 A school
4 Anna Hoover
5 Ladies in Lavender
6 The Windmill Theatre
7 Jack and Sarah
8 Old Deuteronomy
9 Sophie Cookson
10 Mrs Fairfax, the housekeeper

128. Where in the World..... #2

1 China
2 Japan
3 Kefalonia, Greece
4 New York City
5 Australia
6 Thailand
7 Mogadishu, Somalia
8 Slovakia
9 Berlin
10 The Bahamas

129. Gangster Movies

1. Legend
2. The Irishman
3. Public Enemies
4. Shark Tale
5. Naples, Italy
6. His shoes
7. Spider
8. The Tangiers
9. Naomi Watts
10. "He was my father"

130. Will Smith Movies

1. Aladdin
2. J
3. "Welcome to Earth"
4. Margot Robbie
5. After Earth
6. Made in America
7. Sonny
8. "The Butcher of Cadiz"
9. Richard Matheson
10. $105,000

131. 2016

1. Pets
2. Russell Crowe and Ryan Gosling
3. Absolutely Fabulous: The Movie
4. The Girl on the Train
5. Don't Breathe
6. Warren Beatty and Faye Dunaway
7. Zack Snyder
8. Francis
9. AK47 ammunition
10. 90m ski jump

132. Stephen King

1. It
2. The Green Mile
3. Secret Window
4. Pet Sematary
5. Pig's blood
6. Hobbling
7. Dolores Claiborne
8. Gerald's Game
9. Frank Darabont
10. Low Men in Yellow Coats

133. 18 Rated Films

1. Sharon Stone
2. Christian Grey
3. Wrath
4. Eaten by a wolf
5. Mina
6. Three card brag
7. $49m
8. Bed sheets
9. Harriet Vanger
10. To become "the biggest Austrian superstar since Hitler"

134. Name 10 #3

1. 2019: Parasite
2. 2018: Green Book
3. 2017: The Shape of Water
4. 2016: Moonlight
5. 2015: Spotlight
6. 2014: Birdman or (The Unexpected Virtue of Ignorance)
7. 2013: 12 Years a Slave
8. 2012: Argo
9. 2011: The Artist
10. 2010: The King's Speech

135. Al Pacino Movies

1. The Godfather
2. Alaska
3. Danny Collins
4. Big Boy
5. The Merchant of Venice
6. Jack and Jill
7. Bearer bonds
8. Grand Central Station, NYC
9. "The Bank"
10. 1989 Ferrari Mondial

136. 2017

1. T2 Trainspotting
2. Liverpool
3. The Shape of Water
4. Billie Jean King and Bobby Riggs
5. Cogsworth
6. Will Arnett
7. The Mummy
8. "The Sunken Place"
9. Treacher Collins syndrome
10. "Raped while dying", "Still no arrests?", "How come, Chief Willoughby?"

137. Cryptic Clues #2

1. The Game
2. The Perfect Score
3. You've Got Mail
4. Finding Nemo
5. Girl, Interrupted
6. Eye in the sky
7. The Hills have Eyes
8. High Fidelity
9. The Bling Ring
10. Step Up

138. Avengers

1. Loki
2. Joss Whedon
3. Gwyneth Paltrow
4. Falcon
5. Scott Lang
6. Lullaby
7. HYDRA
8. Edward Norton, Mark Ruffalo, Eric Bana
9. Scarlet Witch
10. Squidward

139. Nicolas Cage Movies

1. World Trade Center
2. Ghost Rider
3. The Croods
4. Leaving Las Vegas & Honeymoon in Vegas
5. Jared Leto
6. A snuff film
7. 2 minutes
8. Washington
9. "Everyone Else"
10. Wings of Desire

140. Action #2

1. 10,000 BC
2. Richard Gere
3. Watchmen
4. The Bible
5. Deepwater Horizon
6. G.I.Joe: The Rise of Cobra
7. Kato
8. Jai Courtney
9. A briefcase
10. Kaiju - colossal sea monsters

141. 2018

1. Bohemian Rhapsody
2. Black Panther
3. Anna Kendrick
4. Whitney
5. Game Night
6. Overboard
7. California and Nevada
8. Metropolitan Museum of Art in New York City
9. 'Birds of America' by John James Audubon
10. Isle of Dogs

142. Trilogies

1. Stan Lee
2. Ice hockey
3. Sam Raimi
4. Robert Ludlum
5. Swedish
6. Sean Bean
7. Seth Green
8. Eric Brooks
9. The Wachowskis
10. Three Colours trilogy (Three Colours Blue, White, and Red)

143. Name the Movie From the Quote #3

1. The Hobbit: An Unexpected Journey
2. Taken
3. Unbreakable
4. Bugsy
5. Almost Famous
6. Star Wars: Episode II - Attack of the Clones
7. The Notebook
8. Hail, Ceasar!
9. Bridesmaids
10. Whiplash

144. Keira Knightley Movies

1. Pride and Prejudice
2. Chiwetel Ejiofor and Andrew Lincoln
3. A crossword
4. The Hole
5. Kazuo Ishiguro
6. Balham
7. Rob Hall
8. Sam Worthington
9. Official Secrets
10. Her corset was too tight

145. Anagrams 2010s

1. White House Down
2. Molly's Game
3. Diary of a Wimpy Kid
4. Bad Teacher
5. The Adjustment Bureau
6. The Monuments Men
7. Get Hard
8. Hustlers
9. The Visit
10. American Sniper

146. 2019

1. Avengers: Endgame
2. Us
3. Bong Joon-ho
4. Gemini Man
5. Doctor Sleep
6. She was his babysitter
7. Athur Fleck
8. Midsommar
9. Thomas Edison and George Westinghouse
10. Bait

147. Comedies #3

1. Kindergarten Cop
2. Honey, I Blew Up the Kid
3. Sisters
4. Jane Fonda
5. Ben Bailey Smith
6. Moses the Chihuahua
7. Emma Thompson
8. Wyld Stallyns
9. Fegan Floop
10. Rush

148. Animals #3

1. Killer Whale / Orca
2. Elephant
3. Alvin and the Chipmunks
4. James Corden
5. Sing
6. Alligators
7. Scarlett Johansson
8. Police Officer
9. Sean Hayes
10. Saphira

149. Rotten - Name the Movie with 0% on Rotten Tomatoes

1. Pinocchio
2. Look Who's Talking Now
3. Highlander II: The Quickening
4. Problem Child
5. Cabin Fever
6. Wagons East
7. One Missed Call
8. Derailed
9. Killing Me Softly
10. Stratton

150. Fresh - Name the Movie with 100% on Rotten Tomatoes

1. Toy Story
2. The Wrong Trousers
3. Terminator 2: Judgment Day
4. Paddington 2
5. Man on Wire
6. Wild Bill
7. Leave No Trace
8. Next Goal Wins
9. The Sweet Hereafter
10. Creep 2

I hope you enjoyed this quiz book as much as I enjoyed writing it.

If you could spare a few minutes to leave an honest review it would be much appreciated.

Made in the USA
Coppell, TX
09 December 2023

25757214R00105